WORD Among Us

**A Worship-centered, Lectionary-based
Curriculum for Congregations**

Learner's Guide for Young Elementary

Year 1

United Church Press

Cleveland, Ohio

Thomas E. Dipko	Executive Vice President, UCBHM
Ansley Coe Throckmorton	General Secretary, Division of Education and Publication
Lynne M. Deming	Publisher
Sidney D. Fowler	Editor for Curriculum Resources
Monitta Lowe	Editorial Assistant
Marjorie Pon	Managing Editor
Kelley Baker	Editorial Assistant
Lynn Keller	Business Manager
David M. Perkins	Marketing Director
Cynthia Welch	Production Manager
Martha A. Clark	Art Director
Angela M. Fasciana	Sales and Distribution Manager

Writers

Roberta Cook, an ordained minister in the United Church of Christ, wrote lessons 1–4 and 6–9. She is a graduate of Pacific School of Religion and lives with her husband in Berkeley, California.

Wendy O. Christensen, an elementary school teacher and an accomplished musician, wrote lessons 10–26. She lives with her husband and two young daughters in Telford, Pennsylvania, where she is an active member of St. Paul's Lutheran Church.

Susan Huffman, an ordained minister in the United Church of Christ, wrote lessons 27–52. She serves as co-pastor with her husband at Wright Community Congregational United Church of Christ in Boise, Idaho.

Editor

Carol Birkland, a published author of educational resources, edited this guide. A former director of Christian education, she is currently a professional journalist who lives and works in Cleveland, Ohio.

United Church Press, Cleveland, Ohio 44115
© 1994 by United Church Press
Printed in the United States of America on acid-free paper
First printing, 1994

Design: Kapp & Associates, Inc., Cleveland, Ohio

Cover art: *Jesus Among the Teachers*, detail, Vie de Jesus Mafa, 24 rue du Marechal, Joffre, 78000 Versailles, France. All rights reserved. Used by permission.

Welcome and Information Sheet

Welcome to an exciting year of exploring the Bible with your child in *Word Among Us*.

Your child will hear and explore Bible stories and passages from the lectionary readings for each Sunday. If you are in an adult group using *Word Among Us* or if the lectionary forms the basis for the service of worship for your congregation, your family will have much in common to discuss on Sundays and throughout the week.

The leaders for this group are:

Please complete the form below so the leaders of your child's group have the necessary information to make your child's experience a safe and nurturing one.

Child's name ....

Address ....

Phone ....

Birth date ....

Grade in school ....

Any allergies or health difficulties ....

Special interests ....

....

Parent(s) or guardian ....

Address ....

Phone ....

Are you members of this congregation? ....

Has your child been baptized? ....

What ways might you be able to help or share with the children?

....

....

Contents

Be Opened

Jesus sighed and said, "Ephphatha," that is, "Be opened." And immediately the person's ears were opened, the tongue was released, and the person spoke plainly.

Mark 7:34-35

Duccio di Buoninsegna, *Jesus Opens Eyes of Man Born Blind*, c. 1310, National Gallery of Art, London. Used by permission.

This picture was painted by Duccio di Buoninsegna. It is called *Jesus Opens Eyes of Man Born Blind.* What do you think about when you see this picture?

This is American Sign Language for "be opened." Bring the downturned hands from side by side in front of the chest, upward and outward, ending with the palms facing each other.

Toward the Sea of Galilee

An Antiphonal Rhythm Poem
(to be read responsively by line)

Ephphatha [Ef'-ah-tha], Be opened, Ephphatha, Be opened

Jesus was walking one day.

Ephphatha, Be opened, Ephphatha, Be opened

His friends brought a nonhearing and silent man.

Ephphatha, Be opened, Ephphatha, Be opened

As they walked along the way.

Ephphatha, Be opened, Ephphatha, Be opened

The man could neither speak nor hear.

Ephphatha, Be opened, Ephphatha, Be opened

His sorrow was great, he had little cheer.

Ephphatha, Be opened, Ephphatha, Be opened

Jesus reached out to touch ears and tongue.

Ephphatha, Be opened, Ephphatha, Be opened

And soon new songs of joy were sung.

Ephphatha, Be opened, Ephphatha, Be opened

For the man could speak! The man could hear!

Ephphatha, Be opened, Ephphatha, Be opened

His friends with amazement spread the news far and near.

Ephphatha, Be opened, Ephphatha, Be opened

"Jesus does everything well," they told.

Ephphatha, Be opened, Ephphatha, Be opened

Despite Jesus' asking them to be less bold.

Ephphatha, Be opened, Ephphatha, Be opened

God helps us too to hear and speak.

Ephphatha, Be opened, Ephphatha, Be opened

The justice of God is the Good News we seek!

Ephphatha, Be opened, Ephphatha, Be opened

The man
could speak!
The man
could hear!

at **Home**

As you are with your child this week, make a point of listening to sounds of God's world. If your child has a hearing disadvantage, focus on the rhythms of God's world. Notice and discuss places in your community where people use their voices to speak out for justice and act to free people from their pain as Jesus did. Perhaps you can visit a food kitchen for the homeless or point out another type of caregiving center within the community. What needs exist in your community? Tell your child about them. How does your church help?

Teach
and be
Taught

God has made me a teacher.

Isaiah 50:4-9a

Jesus among the Teachers, Vie de Jesus Mafa, 24 Rue du Marechal Joffre, 78000 Versailles, France. Used by permission.

Jesus, as a boy of twelve, taught the elders of the church.

You and other children have much to teach people in your church.

Little Children, Welcome

Words: Fred Pratt Green, 1973

Music: SAIPAN, by Roy Hopp, 1988

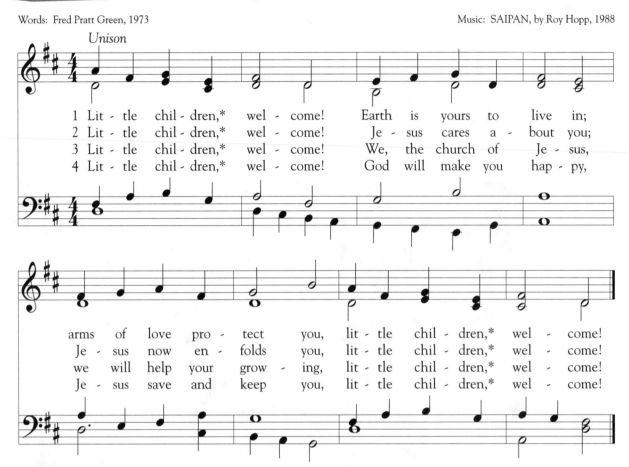

1 Lit - tle chil - dren,* wel - come! Earth is yours to live in;
2 Lit - tle chil - dren,* wel - come! Je - sus cares a - bout you;
3 Lit - tle chil - dren,* wel - come! We, the church of Je - sus,
4 Lit - tle chil - dren,* wel - come! God will make you hap - py,

arms of love pro - tect you, lit - tle chil - dren,* wel - come!
Je - sus now en - folds you, lit - tle chil - dren,* wel - come!
we will help your grow - ing, lit - tle chil - dren,* wel - come!
Je - sus save and keep you, lit - tle chil - dren,* wel - come!

*You may wish to substitute other words as appropriate; for example, "Sisters, brothers, welcome!" "Little sister, welcome!" or "Little brother, welcome!"

▶ *at* Home

This week your child has learned that God calls many different people to be teachers, even children. We listened and learned from each other today during our class time.

Ask your child what he or she taught to the others today. Ask what he or she saw and heard at today's session.

This week, we hope you will be sensitive to ways your child teaches you and others about trust, acceptance, care, and belonging. You may plan to do a caring act together. Or perhaps you will notice a time your child is particularly thoughtful. If that happens, tell your child thank-you. This will help your son or daughter to grow in knowledge of how to spread God's way of love and justice.

Also consider reading the book *Chicken Sunday* (Philomel Books, 1992) by Patricia Polacco to your child.

Welcome the Children

Taking the child in his arms, Jesus said . . .

"whoever welcomes one such child in my name welcomes me. . . ."

Mark 9:35-37

Emil Nolde, *Christ Among the Children* (1910; The Museum of Modern Art, New York. Gift of Dr. W. R. Valentiner). Used by permission.

Prayer:

Dear Jesus, as you welcomed the little children, also welcome us.
Help us to be open to welcome others in your name. Amen

Little Children, Welcome

Words: Fred Pratt Green, 1973

Music: SAIPAN, by Roy Hopp, 1988

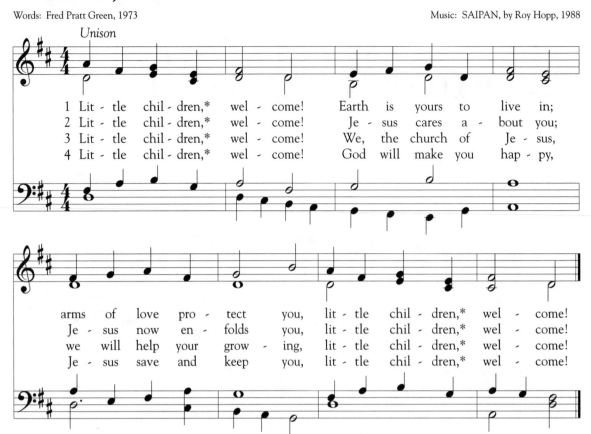

Unison

1 Lit - tle chil - dren,* wel - come! Earth is yours to live in;
2 Lit - tle chil - dren,* wel - come! Je - sus cares a - bout you;
3 Lit - tle chil - dren,* wel - come! We, the church of Je - sus,
4 Lit - tle chil - dren,* wel - come! God will make you hap - py,

arms of love pro - tect you, lit - tle chil - dren,* wel - come!
Je - sus now en - folds you, lit - tle chil - dren,* wel - come!
we will help your grow - ing, lit - tle chil - dren,* wel - come!
Je - sus save and keep you, lit - tle chil - dren,* wel - come!

*You may wish to substitute other words as appropriate; for example, "Sisters, brothers, welcome!" "Little sister, welcome!" or "Little brother, welcome!"

at Home

This is the week for everyone in your family to become especially aware of how Jesus values children.

- Try having a special meal in honor of your child. Let the child choose the menu, help cook the food, and make decorations for the table. Perhaps your child would like to invite a special guest—neighbor, friend, relative or godparent—to share this celebration.

- During the meal, tell stories about your child, such as the story of his or her birth, stories from infancy and early childhood, and the story of how you chose your child's name. Talk about the names you *almost* used—and why you didn't! If your child has been baptized, tell that story.

- After dinner, look at your child's baby book or photographs and baptismal certificate. Sing together, letting your child choose favorite songs. You could include the song on this learner's guide.

- As a family, explore the ways the needs of children are met in your community. Perhaps you have a children's tutorial program, children's hospital, or homeless shelter for families. How could you help by donating time or money through your church for this effort?

- Book resource: Debra Frasier, *On the Day You Were Born* (San Diego: Harcourt Brace Jovanovich, 1991). This is a colorful and poetic story about the wonder and interdependence of all creation—including children.

Deeds of **Power**

Jesus said, "No one who does a deed of power in my name is against us, but is for us."

Mark 9:38-41

Deeds done in the name of Christ are powerful:

- Giving another a cup of water (Mark 9:40)
- Helping new Christians (Mark 9:42-43)
- Working for a more peaceful and safer world (Mark 9:49-50)
- Remembering in prayer people who suffer
- Caring for a sick person
- Caring for the earth
- Finding ways to help people who are hungry

▶ *at* **Home**

This week choose a deed of power from the list above or decide on one of your own. How does God give us power to act in Jesus' name? How do such acts change the world?

Offerings

Jesus offered an unsighted person sight.

He gave the large crowd food to eat.

For the children he had stories,

as well as his lap and loving arms.

Jesus gave a sick man new health.

He offered life to one nearly dead.

To the busy woman he gave an invitation to rest

and to talk, to think, and to learn.

Jesus said to one who had cheated,

"You are forgiven. You can be loving."

He gave to many friendships and new hope.

He was to all a constant companion.

Through my life and my offering of gifts

I can bring sight and food to someone, somewhere.

I can share health and the promise of life.

I can help others to learn and to love.

Like Jesus, I can offer arm loads of caring.

I can offer friendship and forgiveness.

I can share work and hope and joy.

I too can be someone's helpful companion.

Morris Pike, *All Our Days—Laugh and Praise*
(New York: Friendship Press, 1974), 33. Used by permission.

Young Girl's Letter for Peace

Samantha Smith

In 1983, a ten-year-old girl from Maine wrote a letter to the leader of the Soviet Union. Samantha Smith had become worried that there might be a war someday between the United States and the Soviet Union. So Samantha wrote to Yuri Andropov, who was the leader of the government of the Soviet Union.

In her letter Samantha said: "My name is Samantha Smith. I am ten years old. Congratulations on your new job. I have been worrying about Russia and the United States getting into a nuclear war. Are you going to vote to have a war or not? If you aren't, please tell me how you are going to help to not have a war. . . . God made the world for us to live together in peace and not to fight."

Even though all the world leaders receive many more letters from school children than they can answer, Yuri Andropov decided to write a letter to Samantha telling her that he did want peace and inviting her to visit.

Samantha accepted the Soviet leader's invitation, and she traveled to visit the people and places of the Soviet Union. Everywhere she went, friendly people of all ages came to meet the girl who was representing the United States, and to show her that many Soviet people also want peace and that they too are afraid of war.

While the Soviet people gave a message of peace to her, Samantha's warm smile and friendly spirit were also a message of peace to them.

When Samantha came back to the United States, she appeared on television programs to answer questions about her trip to the Soviet Union and to remind people here that the people in the Soviet Union share many of the same hopes and wishes for peace that we have in North America.

The Redoubt, Year 2, Grade 3-4, Celebrate Curriculum
(Louisville, Ky.: Presbyterian Publishing House, 1989), 85.
Used by permission.

The Work of God's Fingers

I look up at the stars, the work of your fingers,
and feel so small. But you made me special.

Psalm 8:3-5

Pretend you are a psalmist.
What would you want to tell
God about such a sky?

Colorful Creator

Text: Ruth Duck, 1992
Music: Carlton Young, 1992

Au-thor of our jour-ney, God of near and far,
praise for tale and dra-ma tell-ing who we are,
strip-ping to the es-sence strug-gles of our day,
times of change and con-flict when we choose our way.

With God's finger,

God made earth, stars, moon, and me.

With my fingers,

I make things wondrous to see.

With my fingers,

I thank God for life and a chance to be.

Aaron Douglas, *The Creation*, 1935, The Howard University Gallery of Art, Permanent Collection, Washington, D.C. Used by permission.

at **Home**

A child is a precious trust,

a gift of God to the world.

To foster a child's uniqueness and

creativity is a joyous, sometimes

messy, but often wonderful and

challenging privilege.

Celebrate the creative gifts of your child. Consider these thoughts from Madeleine L'Engle:

All children are artists, and it is an indictment of our culture that so many of them lose their creativity, their unfettered imaginations, as they grow older. But they start off without self-consciousness as they paint their purple flowers, their anatomically impossible people, their thunderous, sulphurous skies. They don't worry that they may not be as good as Di Chirico or Bracque; they go ahead and say what they want to say. What looks like a hat to a grownup may, to the child artist, be an elephant inside a boa constrictor.

Madeleine L'Engle, *Walking on Water: Reflections on Faith and Art* (Wheaton, Ill.: Harold Shaw Publishers, 1980), 51.

This week, work with your child to be an extension of God's fingers in caring and imagining. You may wish to bake and decorate cookies together and give them to a friend. Or you may wish to provide your child with some art materials and space to create. How about building something together? Pray with your child this week. Give God thanks for the signs of creation and the gifts of your child's creativity.

Gracious Justice

Hate evil and
love good, and
establish justice.

Amos 5:14-15

A True Story about God and Ruby Bridges

Ruby Bridges was six years old. By chance, Ruby was the first black child to attend what had been an all-white school. It was terrible for her. She did not give up.

And it was Ruby's mother who explained the reason that Ruby was able to endure such a long and terrible experience. Ruby's mother said, "…God was helping Ruby, and we thought you'd want to know that."

Ruby was only six years old, but she knew God was with her. God helped her to be very brave. God helped her to do the right thing. God helped her to forgive those who were cruel to her. This story is Ruby's story. It is her mother's and father's story. But it is also God's story.

Ruby's story has helped many people work for justice as they discover God's presence in their lives.

Robert Coles, *The Moral Life of Children*, (Boston: Houghton Mifflin, 1986).

❖ *at* **Home**

Children who experience that God is with them possess the greatest gift that anyone can ever know. This week, ask your child to tell you the story of Ruby Bridges that he or she heard in class. Share with your child a story of something that was very hard for you. How did you experience God's presence with you in that?

You may wish to check your library or a bookstore for a story that is similar to Ruby's. One such story is: *Gwen Everett, Li'l Sis and Uncle Willie* (New York: Rizzoli International Publications, Inc., 1991).

God
is
my
shepherd

Psalm 23

Psalm 23 is a poem and song about the sure presence of God. People who work for goodness and justice find great meaning and help by repeating it. Read it together from your Bible at home. Also, learn this version together:

God is my shepherd, I shall not want;

God makes me lie down in green pastures,

and leads me beside still waters;

God restores my soul.

God leads me in paths of righteousness

for God's name sake.

Even though I walk through the valley of

the shadow of death,

I fear no evil;

for you are with me;

your rod and your staff,

they comfort me.

You prepare a table before me

in the presence of my enemies;

you anoint my head with oil,

my cup overflows.

Surely goodness and mercy shall follow me

all the days of my life;

and I shall dwell in the house of God

forever.

National Council of the Churches of Christ in the U.S.A.,
An Inclusive-Language Lectionary: Readings for Year B, rev. ed.
(New York: The Pilgrim Press, 1987), 132.

True Greatness

So Jesus called the disciples and said to them, "… whoever wishes to become great among you must be your servant, and whoever wishes to be first among you must be slave of all."

Mark 10:42-45

The Story of Saint Francis

 long time ago, there was a boy named Francis who was the son of a wealthy merchant who lived in the town of Assisi in Italy. Because his parents were rich, Francis grew up in a grand home and wore very fine clothes. He had many friends and spent most of his time at parties or having fun with his friends. He spent his parents' money very freely.

When he was a teenager, he ran off to battle where he was injured. By the time he returned home, he had also become ill. His injuries and illness worried him, so he began to pray. God spoke to him through his prayers. Francis heard the voice of Christ speak, "Francis, rebuild my church."

Well, Francis didn't have any money of his own, but he felt that he had to answer Christ's request, so he stole bolts of cloth from his father, sold them and gave the money he received to the church.

He then ran away. His father was hurt and angry that his son should do such a thing. When

Giovanni Bellini, *St. Francis in Ecstasy*, c. 1485, The Frick Collection, New York. Used by permission.

Francis returned later, looking like a beggar because he had no money of his own, his father took him before the Bishop to see what should be done with the young man.

The Bishop told Francis that God does not want stolen money. He asked Francis to return the money to his father.

Francis listened to the Bishop's words and must have felt sorry. He said that he would not only give the money back to his father, but he would also return everything he had ever received from him. Then he stepped behind a curtain and took off all of his clothes and laid them, with the money, at his father's feet. The Bishop gave Francis a brown monk's robe to wear.

From that moment on, Francis claimed God as his father and gave his life in service to God. He spent his whole life living in poverty and caring for the poor. He also spent time caring for God's animal creatures. As he turned his life to service, his spirit grew. He believed that God would always provide for him.

The Prayer of Saint Francis

God, make us instruments of your peace.

Where there is hatred, let us sow love.

Where there is injury, pardon.

Where there is doubt, faith.

Where there is despair, hope.

Where there is sadness, joy.

Attributed to St. Francis of Assisi, from *With All God's People: The New Ecumenical Prayer Cycle*, comp. John Carden (Geneva: WCC Publications, 1989). Used by permission.

peace

love

pardon

faith

hope

joy

at **Home**

What is true greatness? Your child is busy trying to establish an identity, busy learning to be assertive, and busy finding self-esteem. Yet it is not too early for your child to learn about true greatness as Jesus and Saint Francis spoke of it and lived it.

- This week, for nighttime or mealtime prayers, use the Prayer of Saint Francis at the top of this page. Your child has recreated a prayer based on this. Please display it prominently at home for a while.

- Read together the story of Francis on this learner's guide.

- Additional reading: Tomie de Paola, *Francis, the Poor Man of Assisi* (New York: Holiday House, 1982)

A Great Company

See, I am going to bring them from the land of the north, and gather them from the farthest parts of the earth. . . . A great company, they shall return here.

Jeremiah 31:8-9a

I am one of the company,	clap, clap
The company, the company,	
I am one of the company,	stomp, stomp
God's great company, that's me!	
We are some of the company,	clap, clap
The company, the company,	
We are some of the company,	stomp, stomp
God's great company, that's us!	
All are part of the company,	clap, clap
The company, the company,	
All are part of the company,	stomp, stomp
God's great company,	pause and shout
that's all!	clap, clap, stomp, stomp, clap, clap

God's Great Company

23

Colorful Creator

Text: Ruth Duck, 1992
Music: Carlton Young, 1992

Au - thor of our jour - ney, God of near and far,

praise for tale and dra - ma tell - ing who we are,

strip - ping to the es - sence strug - gles of our day,

times of change and con - flict when we choose our way.

✳ *at* **Home**

The prophet Jeremiah tells us that God gather's God's own into one great company. Children are natural gatherers. They usually like the activity that comes with gathering and often find security within a group.

Today the children learned that God gathers people into a great company of believers and within that company there is love and safety. To reinforce that concept with your child this week, consider taking time to gather the whole family together to sing a song or a hymn, or to pray. As you do, mention that you are gathering in God's name as part of God's great company.

Gather in God's name

All Your **Heart,**
All Your **Soul,**
All Your **Mind!**

One of the scribes . . . asked Jesus, "Which commandment is the first of all?" Jesus answered, "The first is, 'Hear O Israel: God is one; you shall love your God with all your heart, and with all your mind, and with all your strength.' The second is this, 'You shall love your neighbor as yourself.' There is no other commandment greater than these."

Mark 12:28-31

Dorothea Lange, *Migrant Mother*, 1936, Nipomo, California (Library of Congress). Used by permission.

The photographer Dorothea Lange saw the beauty and uniqueness of this mother, worn and tired from long hours of work in the fields with too little pay. She also "caught" with her camera the love between her and her tousled children.

The Great Commandment

Hear, O Israel: God is one;

You shall love your God with all your heart,

and with all your soul,

and with all your mind,

and with all your strength,

and you shall love your neighbor as yourself.

Little Children, Welcome

Words: Fred Pratt Green, 1973

Music: SAIPAN, by Roy Hopp, 1988

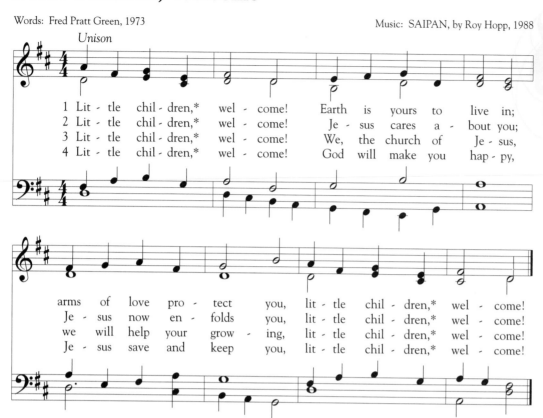

Unison

1 Lit - tle chil - dren,* wel - come! Earth is yours to live in;
2 Lit - tle chil - dren,* wel - come! Je - sus cares a - bout you;
3 Lit - tle chil - dren,* wel - come! We, the church of Je - sus,
4 Lit - tle chil - dren,* wel - come! God will make you hap - py,

arms of love pro - tect you, lit - tle chil - dren,* wel - come!
Je - sus now en - folds you, lit - tle chil - dren,* wel - come!
we will help your grow - ing, lit - tle chil - dren,* wel - come!
Je - sus save and keep you, lit - tle chil - dren,* wel - come!

*You may wish to substitute other words as appropriate; for example, "Sisters, brothers, welcome!" "Little sister, welcome!" or "Little brother, welcome!"

at Home

Your young child is busy learning about life from your actions and the actions of others—rules and examples that he or she will live by for a lifetime. This week, talk with your child about God's Great Commandment. Share with your child what it means to you to love God and neighbor as self.

In Jewish tradition, the first commandment is called the Shema. Families keep it written in their homes—on their door posts.

Together, think about some people you know who are different from you in education, race, income, or life style. Why are these people, like you, children of God? Why are they "neighbors"? Is that hard to understand sometimes?

Consider including the Great Commandment as you pray with your child this week.

Love Your Neighbor!

Fullness of the Gift

A poor widow came and put in two small copper coins, which are worth a penny. Then Jesus called the disciples and said to them, "Truly I tell you, this poor widow has put in more than all those who are contributing to the treasury… She out of her poverty has put in everything she had, all she had to live on."

Mark 12:41-44

Paula Modersohn-Becker, *Old Peasant Woman*, 1906, gift of Robert H. Tannahill, © The Detroit Institute of Arts. Used by permission.

The artist is telling you a lot about this woman. What can you tell from the expression on her face? What can you tell from her hands? What might she be thinking about?

The Bible Tells of God's Great Love

Words: Betty Doughman, 1961; alt. 1983

Music from Thomas Este's
Whole Book of Psalms, 1592

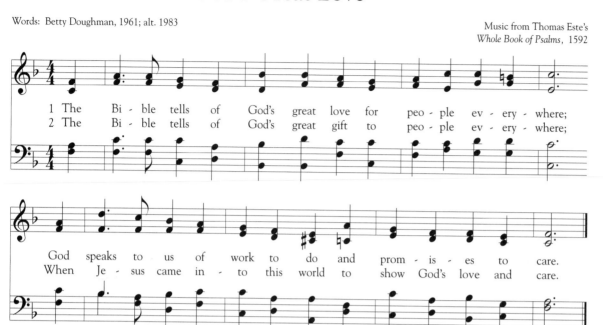

1 The Bi - ble tells of God's great love for peo - ple ev - ery - where;
2 The Bi - ble tells of God's great gift to peo - ple ev - ery - where;

God speaks to us of work to do and prom - is - es to care.
When Je - sus came in - to this world to show God's love and care.

at Home

We are surrounded by God's gifts. Your child is one of God's precious gifts to you as you are to your child.

This week, make a special point of giving time to your child. Read together. Play together. Prepare a meal or a treat together. Make a shopping list together. It can be almost anything. Very often a job that can be done more efficiently alone is a real source of learning and communion for your child.

When your child brings things home from school, give praise and encouragement. These offerings represent the child's efforts and are of great value.

This week you might think of ways to give to others in your community. Perhaps you have clothes to give away. Perhaps your child has outgrown some puzzles or has something to donate to a child in greater need. Perhaps you can give food to a social agency.

Your child may particularly enjoy giving to God's creatures. You might find an opportunity this week to feed the birds.

Pray with your child. Give thanks for God's many gifts.

God Among Us

I keep God always before me;

because God is at my right hand,

I shall not be moved.

Psalm 16:5-8

Angel De mi guarda Dulce Compania, no me aBanDones, ni De Día. Cuatro esquinas tiene mi cama, cuatro angeles me cuidan ni De Noche, me cuidan, con Las once mil candelas que se alumBró eL santicimo sacramento DeL altar. Amen. Jesus, Maria y Jose. Angel De mi guarda, Dulce compania no me aBanDones, a Jesucristo a mi caBecera. Si me Duermo Si me muero me veloran,

Gertrude Myrrh Reagan, Angel de mi Guarda,
as reproduced in Woman of Power: Art as Activism, 6
(Spring 1987): 20.

God protects us and stays with us. This painting shows a guardian angel as a sweet companion.

Trust Walk

Take my hand and lead me,
    I will trust your care.
Take my hand and lead me,
    I will follow there.
Take my hand and lead me,
    God, the parent kind.
Take my hand and lead me,
    To your will I bind.

O God, Hear My Prayer

from Psalm 101
Words and music: the Taizé Community, 1981

O Lord, hear my prayer, O Lord, hear my prayer: when I call an-swer me.

O Lord, hear my prayer, O Lord, hear my prayer, come and lis-ten to me.

Your Poem

_____

_____

_____

_____

_____

_____

_____

_____

_____

_____

_____

_____

_____

at Home

There are many things your child can show you on this learner's guide. Ask your child to read the poem with you that was written by the children today. Talk about the images that the children used in their poem. Are some of your child's concerns expressed? Talk about these concerns and about how God is always present in our lives.

This week, you and your child can extend the idea that some things are present, but may not be seen. Look for examples in nature. For instance, you might show your child a lima bean or kidney bean and talk about what might be inside it. Split one open. Then, place an intact bean in a jar. Hold it next to the glass with a wet paper towel. Soon, you will see roots and a stem. Plant it in a pot. Talk about how the bean has everything it needs to grow inside it.

Pray with your child. Thank God for always being with you.

I Bring the Truth

Pilate asked Jesus, "So you are a king?" Jesus answered, "You say that I am a king. For this I was born, and for this I came into the world, to testify to the truth."

John 18:33-38

Peter Spier, *People* (New York: Delacorte Press, 1980). © 1980 by Peter Spier. Used by permission of Bantam Doubleday Dell Books for Young Readers.

This picture shows what variety there is in people. It is a celebration of our differences and tells about respecting one another. It points to the *truth* about our differences. In today's lesson Pilate wanted to know who Jesus was. Jesus said that he came into the word to tell about truth. Jesus told Pilate that those who believe in truth—believe that God represents truth—belong to God.

One truth is, even though we are all different, we all belong to God.

Little Children, Welcome

Words: Fred Pratt Green, 1973

Music: Roy Hopp, 1988

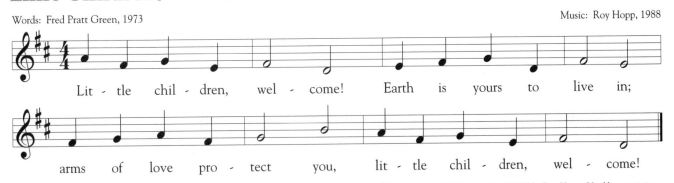

Lit - tle chil - dren, wel - come! Earth is yours to live in;

arms of love pro - tect you, lit - tle chil - dren, wel - come!

Pilate Questions Jesus

Leader: Pilate is a powerful man. He rules over many people. His job is to keep things peaceful even though many groups of people disagree about many things. An angry group brings Jesus to the guards.

Crowd: Here is Jesus. He is dangerous.

Leader: The guards bring Jesus before Pilate.

Pilate: What has he done?

Crowd: He is a criminal. Get rid of him.

Pilate: (to Jesus) Are you a king?

Jesus: You say that I am.

Leader: Pilate does not think that Jesus seems dangerous.
Who is Jesus, really?
Whom should he believe?

Pilate: (to Jesus) What is truth?

Leader: (Leave a silence.) Jesus does not answer. Jesus is killed soon afterward. The truth is that God loves us so much that God gave Jesus' life for us.

truth

at Home

Children know a lot of things. They can be good teachers for adults. They often express themselves without complicating the matter.

This week, ask your child to tell you about the picture on the other side of this learner's guide. If possible, read together the book from which it has been reproduced and talk about it. It can be found in most libraries and bookstores. There are many ideas you may enjoy discussing in this book.

Talk also about God and how God loves us. Take turns finishing the sentence, "I know God loves me because…" Your child may think of many ways new to you.

Pray with your child this week. Give God thanks for sending us Jesus.

Behold the Signs

Jesus said, "There will be signs in the sun, the moon, and the stars, and on the earth. . . . The powers of the heavens will be shaken."

Luke 21:25-26

Paul Chesley, *Forked Lightning Reflected in Lake*, Tony Stone Worldwide. Used by permission.

Do you see God in nature? Sometimes people talk about lightning as a sign of God's power. It is a powerful force full of light and electricity. It can be frightening and it can be beautiful.

My **Soul** Gives Glory to My **God**

Melody from *Kentucky Harmony*, 1816

Words by Miriam Therese Winter, 1987; rev. 1993

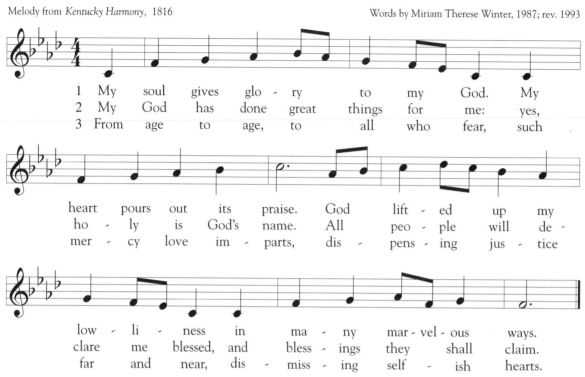

1 My soul gives glo - ry to my God. My
2 My God has done great things for me: yes,
3 From age to age, to all who fear, such

heart pours out its praise. God lift - ed up my
ho - ly is God's name. All peo - ple will de -
mer - cy love im - parts, dis - pens - ing jus - tice

low - li - ness in ma - ny mar - vel - ous ways.
clare me blessed, and bless - ings they shall claim.
far and near, dis - miss - ing self - ish hearts.

℘ ℘ ℘ ℘ *at* **Home**

Advent is a time of hope for things to come—not just presents and the trappings of Christmas, but hope for humanity as well.

This week, perhaps you and your child can share hope with someone else. Sometimes, the simplest gestures are appreciated the most. If you are musical, perhaps you can learn this Advent song and sing it with you child for a neighbor or grandparent. Another song that you already know would might also be appropriate.

Some people's lives do, indeed, seem dark. Is there something you and your child could do to bring them some light? A visit? A card? An invitation?

If your church has an outreach program, see if there is a way for you both to contribute.

Explore all the sources of light in your life with your child and when you pray with your child this week, give thanks to God for them.

Here are some additional ideas to help your child anticipate the birth of Jesus:

- Use an Advent calendar each day during Advent to help build anticipation.

- Set up a nativity scene or creche. Add one or two figures a week to the arrangement. The baby Jesus could be put in the manger on Christmas.

- Look through the hymnal and point out to your child that there are separate sections for Advent hymns and for Christmas hymns. Look at the words of some of the Advent hymns and try to find words that talk about "coming" and "preparation."

Prepare the Way

Frans Pourbus the Elder, *Sermon of St. John the Baptist,* Musée des Beaux-Arts, Valenciennes, France (Photographie Giraudon/Art Resource, N.Y.). Used by permission.

The artist, Pourbus, painted John talking to a crowd of people. Look at John's face. Is he excited about what he is saying? How about his listeners? What do they seem to think about what he is saying?

The word of God came to John son of Zechariah in the wilderness . . . "Prepare the way of the Lord, make the paths of the Lord straight."

Luke 3:2b-4

My Soul Gives Glory to My God

My soul gives glory to my God,

My heart pours out its praise.

God lifted up my lowliness

in many marvelous ways.

Miriam Therese Winter, 1987, alt., hymn lyrics, © 1987 Medical Mission Sisters. Used by permission.

A D V E N T

Waiting and hoping,
we light a candle.
Getting ready
for Jesus.

This poem has exactly seventeen syllables.
It is a Japanese form of poetry called haiku.
Can you write one?

Frans Pourbus the Elder, *Sermon of St. John the Baptist,* detail, Musée des Beaux-Arts, Valenciennes, France (Photographie Giraudon/Art Resource, N.Y.). Used by permission.

⟲ ⟲ ⟲ ⟲ *at* **Home**

Children seem to know when something is in the air. They read the signs of preparation in a multitude of ways—the smell of baking cookies, the sight of more mail arriving, the sound of secret whispers, and even the effect of short tempers.

It is especially important to include children during holiday preparations, but it can be hard to find the time. Here are some suggestions for things to do with your children that can enhance your preparations. In some cases, they may be continued independently by your child:

- Make cards together. A simple card that is handmade (especially by a child) can mean a lot to the recipient. You can help cut simple shapes from construction paper and the child can glue them or you might just help with ideas. Candles, wreaths, a fir tree, a stable, a star are all designs that a young child can manage with a little help. You may also

wish to cut out pictures from last year's Christmas cards. The child may not want to make the dozens that you may need, but whatever is made will be very special. You might want to keep one to look at together and remember next year.

- Make a list of people to whom you and your child would like to send cards. Consider keeping this list from year to year.

- Make wrapping paper. You can use computer paper, newsprint, butcher paper, or even shopping bags. Cookie cutters can be used for designs. Dip them in non-toxic paint and use them to make a pattern on the paper, or cut an apple or potato in half, carve a simple star design, dip it in paint, and stamp it on the paper.

- Light an Advent candle before dinner and pray with your child. Give God thanks for what is to come.

Rejoice in the Lord always; again I will say, Rejoice. Let your gentleness be known to everyone. The Lord is near.

Philippians 4:4-5

Rejoice!

The artist is showing people who are busy and active doing something. What do you think they are doing? How do you think they feel?

Jacob Lawrence, *Harriet Tubman Series No.4*, Hampton University Museum, Hampton, Virginia. Used by permission.

My Soul Gives Glory to My God

My soul gives glory to my God,

My heart pours out its praise.

God lifted up my lowliness

in many marvelous ways.

Miriam Therese Winter, 1987, alt., hymn lyrics,
© 1987 Medical Mission Sisters. Used by permission.

at **Home**

The Apostle Paul,

in his letter to the Philippians,

told his congregation

to rejoice! Today in class,

your child rejoiced.

Young children can be like compressed springs. They can be balls of potential energy. This week, in the increasing activity of preparations, why not set one evening aside for play with your child. You could ask, "What would you really like to play the most this evening?" You can browse over the shelves with your child and talk about the games you've played. Your child may pick one from years ago that you might think no longer holds any interest for the child. Your child may pick one that you have played so often that it holds no interest for you. Maybe nothing looks right to your child this evening.

Perhaps you could teach a game you learned as a child. Here are some suggestions that may be fun for you and your child:

- **Hide and seek in the house**
- **Scissors, paper, rock**
- **Hide an object, give hot and cold clues**
- **Charades—guess the animal, book title, and so on**

You might also like to make a people chain with your child, such as the one your child brought home today. Perhaps it would be fun to color the figures together wearing clothes to look like members of the family and friends. Does your child have a favorite shirt or dress? Do you?

What does this have to do with Advent? Playing is an expression of love. Giving joy is an expression of the joy given you. Teaching things you have learned is an expression of sharing. Asking your child to choose is an expression of respect. All of these are part of Advent.

Rejoice with your child this week!

Blessed

Käthe Kollowitz, *Maria and Elizabeth*, 1928,
© 1993 ARS, New York/VG Bild-Kunst,
Germany. Used by permission.

In those days Mary set out and went
with haste to a Judean town in the hill
country, where she entered the house
of Zechariah and greeted Elizabeth.
When Elizabeth heard Mary's greeting,
the child leaped in her womb.

Luke 1:39-41

My Soul Gives Glory to My God

Melody from *Kentucky Harmony*, 1816

Words by Miriam Therese Winter, 1987; rev. 1993

1 My soul gives glo-ry to my God. My
2 My God has done great things for me: yes,
3 From age to age, to all who fear, such

heart pours out its praise. God lift-ed up my
ho-ly is God's name. All peo-ple will de-
mer-cy love im-parts, dis-pens-ing jus-tice

low-li-ness in ma-ny mar-vel-ous ways.
clare me blessed, and bless-ings they shall claim.
far and near, dis-miss-ing self-ish hearts.

at **Home**

This week's lesson is about a visit. Perhaps you and your child can give the gift of a visit to someone during the week. Perhaps your church has a list of elderly or ill people who may not see visitors often and would really appreciate your company for a little while. Perhaps you know someone whom you have not had the time to visit recently.

If at all possible, bring the person something you and your child have made. The ornament your child made today in class is one good example of an easy project. This type of ornament is commonly made by Polish children and is called a sniezynka (shne-zh-in-ka), which means "snowflake."

- Cut two white paper circles and one colored paper circle for each ornament (about four inches in diameter).

- Fold the white paper circle in half, then in half again. You can fold it in half a third time if it doesn't seem too thick to cut.

- Cut into the folded sides. Here are some possible patterns:

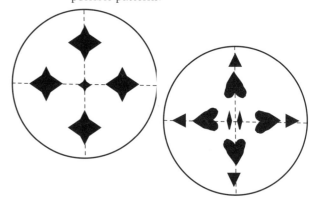

- Repeat with the other white paper circle. (It can be a different design.)

- Unfold the patterns and glue to the colored paper along with a ribbon from which to hang the ornament.

Even the smallest of gifts from children can give a very big message. Let your child know how important the gesture is and how much it is appreciated.

Glory to God!

And suddenly there was with the angel, a multitude of the heavenly host, praising God and saying, "Glory to God in the highest heaven, and on earth peace among those whom God favors!"

Luke 2:13-14

Henry Ossawa Tanner, *Angels Appearing Before the Shepherds*, 1910, National Museum of American Art, Smithsonian Institution, Washington, D.C. (Art Resource, N.Y.). Used by permission.

This painting shows the angels announcing Christ's birth to the shepherds. How do you think the shepherds felt? How do you think you would feel if you had been there?

Sing A Different

Words and music: The Iona Community, 1987

1 Sing a dif-ferent song now Christ-mas is here,
sing a song of peo-ple know-ing God's near:
The Mes - si - ah is born in the
face of our scorn, sing a dif-ferent song to
wel - come and warn.

2 Shout a dif-ferent shout now Christ-mas is here,
shout a shout of joy and gen - u - ine cheer:
Fill the earth and the sky with the
news from on high, shout a dif-ferent shout that
all may come by.

3 Love a dif-ferent love now Christ-mas is here,
love with-out con - di - tion, love with - out fear:
With the hum - ble and poor, with the
shy and un - sure, love a dif-ferent love. Let
Christ be the cure!

at Home

Christmas is a time for sharing. Some of this sharing is simply a verbal exchange with your child. You might ask your child, for example, to draw a picture of their favorite thing about Christmas and tell you about it. You could do the same.

This is also a time to include the larger global family in your gift-giving. Listed below are some ways to show your child how you can share with others. Put money aside until you find an organization you wish to donate to. Your church probably has a list of local social agencies or overseas peace projects and can help you find information.

- Challenge your family to decrease your utilities bill next month and contribute the amount saved to a special charity, or church.

- Save money earned through recycling.

- Plan a simple soup supper and save the difference in the cost of the meal.

- Select some belongings to either donate out-right or sell at a yard sale and donate the proceeds.

- Encourage your child to donate a part of his or her allowance or earned money.

The way small contributions add up sometimes sur-prises children and adults. Encouraging children to be sensitive to the needs of others would truly be a great Christmas gift.

Jesus, Amazing Child

After three days Mary and Joseph found Jesus in the temple, sitting among the teachers, listening to them and asking them questions. And all who heard him were amazed at his understanding and his answers.

Luke 2:46-47

The artist shows us some people talking to one another.

▶ Can you imagine what each one is saying?

▶ Is one person the teacher, or more than one?

Jesus Among the Teachers, Vie de Jesus Mafa, 24 rue du Marechal, Joffre, 78000 Versailles, France. All rights reserved. Used by permission.

Jesus taught the word of God at the age of twelve to a group of elders. Today we celebrate the first step of his ministry.

Sing A Different Song

Words and music: The Iona Community, 1987

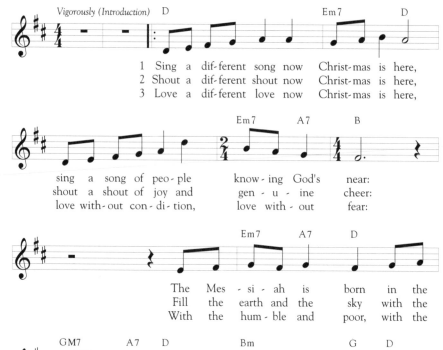

1 Sing a dif-ferent song now Christ-mas is here,
sing a song of peo-ple know-ing God's near:
The Mes - si - ah is born in the
face of our scorn, sing a dif-ferent song to
wel - come and warn.

2 Shout a dif-ferent shout now Christ-mas is here,
shout a shout of joy and gen - u - ine cheer:
Fill the earth and the sky with the
news from on high, shout a dif-ferent shout that
all may come by.

3 Love a dif-ferent love now Christ-mas is here,
love with-out con - di - tion, love with - out fear:
With the hum - ble and poor, with the
shy and un - sure, love a dif-ferent love. Let
Christ be the cure!

at **Home**

Young children are likely to think of Jesus as a friend and are eager to learn about his childhood. This week's lesson has been about Jesus' development as a student and teacher of God's word.

You child is familiar with the role of a student, but how often do we ask our children if there is something in particular they would like to learn from us? This week, try to find some time to discover with your child if there is something the child would like you to teach.

Your child may be unfamiliar with the role of teacher. How often do we ask our child to teach us something? Try to find some time to discover with your child if there is something the child could teach you.

The list may start out small and grow during the week. Enjoy the endless possibilities! Perhaps the ideas on your lists can extend beyond your home to others.

Child: Things to teach

_____

_____

_____

_____

Adult: Things to teach

_____

_____

_____

_____

Jesus Baptized

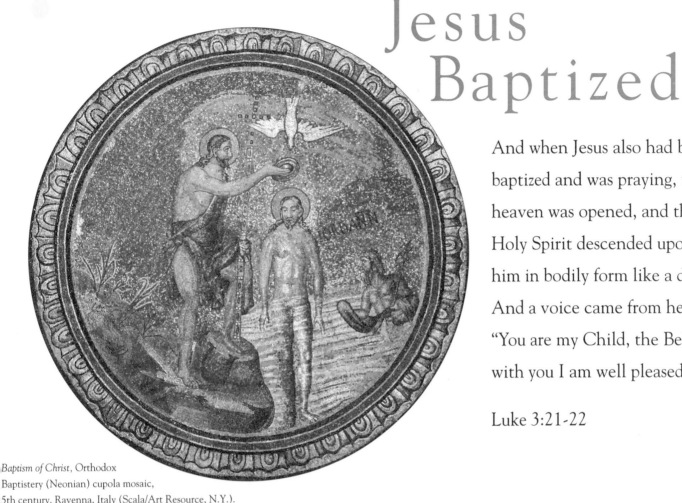

And when Jesus also had been baptized and was praying, the heaven was opened, and the Holy Spirit descended upon him in bodily form like a dove. And a voice came from heaven, "You are my Child, the Beloved; with you I am well pleased."

Luke 3:21-22

Baptism of Christ, Orthodox Baptistery (Neonian) cupola mosaic, 5th century, Ravenna, Italy (Scala/Art Resource, N.Y.). Used by permission.

This is a mosaic showing John baptizing Jesus. Mosaics are pictures made up of small, colorful pieces of tile, glass, or stone. This one was made five hundred years ago by Greek artists. Which figure is John? Can you imagine the words John is saying to Jesus?

Our song: ....

....

....

....

....

Can you write more verses about water and baptism?

The Bible Tells of God's Great Love

Words: Betty Doughman, 1961; alt. 1983

Music from Thomas Este's
Whole Book of Psalms, 1592

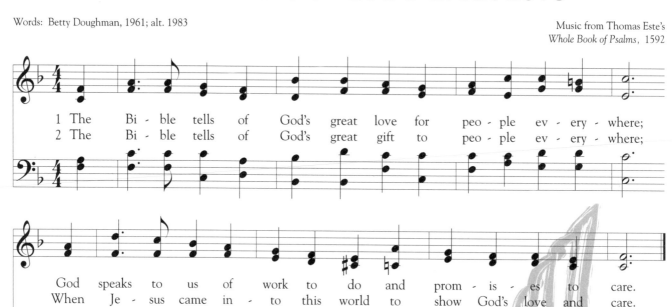

1 The Bi - ble tells of God's great love for peo - ple ev - ery - where;
2 The Bi - ble tells of God's great gift to peo - ple ev - ery - where;

God speaks to us of work to do and prom - is - es to care.
When Je - sus came in - to this world to show God's love and care.

at **Home**

Baptism is a most important event in the life of Christians. It indicates entrance into the church of Christ as well as into the family of God. Baptism recognizes God as life-giving and sustaining.

This would be a good time to share baptismal memories with your child. Perhaps you have records or stories about the baptisms of family members. It is still possible to trace family lineage through baptismal records, which were often more accurate than birth certificates.

If your child has been baptized, try to find the certificate and any other records that may be tucked away. Do you have pictures or do you remember how your child behaved that day? What was the date? In addition to celebrating birthdays, perhaps it would become a meaningful family tradition to also celebrate baptismal birthdays. It is not necessarily the occasion for a cake and presents, but rather it may be an occasion to remember God's gifts by being generous to others or by helping preserve the earth.

If your child has not been baptized, talk about your own baptism or that of someone you know. Describe what happened and how you felt.

You might read over the service of baptism found in the hymnal with your child this week. Jot down any questions you or your child have to ask the pastor or your child's group leader.

The **Wedding** at **Cana**

Cana Jesus Turns Water into Wine, Vie de Jesus Mafa,
4 rue du Marechal, Joffre, 78000 Versailles, France.

When the steward tasted the water that had become wine, …the steward called the bridegroom and said to him, "…you have kept the good wine until now." Jesus did this, the first of his signs, in Cana of Galilee, and revealed his glory.

John 2:9-11

How did the artist show that these people are **celebrating** and having **fun**?

What are the children doing?

If you were in this picture, what would **you** be doing?

The Bible Tells of God's Great Love

The Bible tells of God's great love
For people ev'rywhere;
God speaks to us of work to do
And promises to care.

The Bible tells of God's great gift
To people ev'rywhere;
When Jesus came into this world
To show God's love and care.

Betty Doughman, from *Songs and Hymns for Primary Children*. Words (c) 1961 by W. L. Jenkins, renewed 1991. Used by permission of Westminster/John Knox.

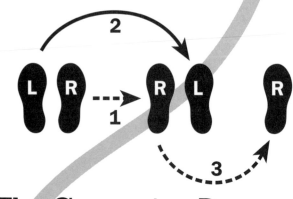

The Grapevine Dance

This grapevine step is a common element in folk dances in the Middle East. It can be done in a circle or a line, holding hands, and has four steps:

1 **Step to the right with the right foot.**

2 **Cross the left foot in front of the right.**

3 **Step again to the right with the right foot.**

4 **Cross the left foot in back of the right.**

at **Home**

Your child is learning about Jesus' life. This week, rejoice with your child that Jesus is a constant companion. Put on some music and try this dance, which has been popular for hundreds of years. Wind around the furniture in your home. Experiment with new steps.

You can encourage your child to have a dialogue with Jesus by saying nighttime prayers together. Take turns saying words of thanks. Your child would probably like to know what you are grateful for and what your hopes are.

Fulfilled in Your Hearing

Jesus stood up to read,…

"The Spirit of God is upon me,

because God has anointed me

to bring good news to the poor,…

proclaim release to the captives and

recovery of sight to the blind."

Luke 4:16c, 18

Rembrandt van Rijn, *Christ Preaching*, 1656, bequest of
Mrs. H. O. Havemeyer, 1929, the H. O. Havemeyer Collection
(29.107.18), The Metropolitan Museum of Art, New York.
All rights reserved. Used by permission.

This is a drawing of the Isaiah scroll,

the oldest copy of a complete book of the Old Testament. It is made of seventeen pieces of leather sewn together and was found in a cave near the Dead Sea. It was found in 1947 by a boy who was herding his goats. Scrolls were protected by placing them in jars and hiding them in caves.

        at **Home**

Your child is probably familiar with the roles of teachers and students. Today's reading is about the teaching of Jesus. Ask your child this week what your family can learn from Jesus' words. Then think through various ways that even a young child can feel effective in helping the world community.

Your church may have some suggestions for local relief efforts. In addition to these, the following book has numerous suggestions for children, families, and larger groups:

> Tracy Apple Howard, *Kids Ending Hunger: What Can We Do?* (Kansas City: Andrews & McMeel, Universal Press Syndicate, 1992).

You can also write to the authors at this address:

> Andrews & McMeel,
> Universal Press Syndicate
> 4900 Main Street
> Kansas City, MO 64112

The point is that there is something that everyone can do. Help your child to feel that everyone's efforts make a difference. Show your child how to have a caring response to other people.

Accept or Reject?

And Jesus said, "Truly I tell you, no prophet is accepted in the prophet's hometown."

Luke 4:24

The artist Henry Ossawa Tanner has painted a picture of Jesus as he is deep in thought. What are some things you would like to tell Jesus? What are some things you would like to ask Jesus?

Henry Ossawa Tanner, *The Saviour*, c. 1900-1905, National Museum of American Art, Smithsonian Institution, Washington, D.C. (Art Resource, N.Y.). Used by permission.

The Bible Tells of God's Great Love

Words: Betty Doughman, 1961; alt. 1983

Music from Thomas Este's
Whole Book of Psalms, 1592

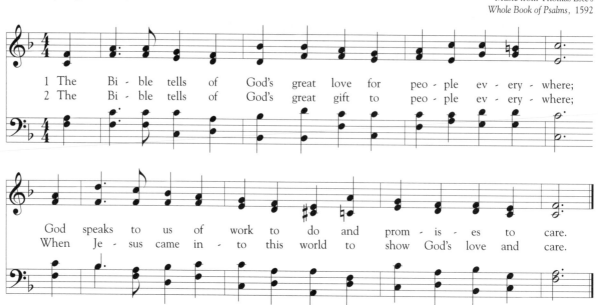

1 The Bi - ble tells of God's great love for peo - ple ev - er - y - where;
2 The Bi - ble tells of God's great gift to peo - ple ev - er - y - where;

God speaks to us of work to do and prom - is - es to care.
When Je - sus came in - to this world to show God's love and care.

Words copyright © 1961, by W. L. Jenkins; from *Songs and Hymns for Primary Children*. Used by permission of The Westminster Press.

at **Home**

This Epiphany season, your child is learning about Jesus through stories, songs, and pictures. You can encourage these explorations by looking at various pictures of Jesus and talking about the different ways Jesus has been depicted over the centuries in many cultures. Perhaps your church has a library where you and your child can browse together.

Today's reading in Luke takes place in Nazareth, Jesus' hometown. Usually a hometown has much meaning for an individual.

Try to find an opportunity to discuss your hometown with your child this week and bring out some old pictures, if you have any. Is your child's hometown the same as yours? Show your child various locations on the map relative to your child's hometown.

Jesus traveled few miles compared to the number that many people travel today. Yet each town had a distinct character. How would you describe the character of your hometown? Ask your child to do the same.

It might be an interesting project to begin a family history book with your child. It can begin with your generation, your child's generation, or far in the past. It can be factual or a record of impressions. It can include photographs or drawings. Place the book in an accessible spot so that entries can be made at any time. Years from now, it will be fun to look over a collaborative record of landmark events in your family's life.

Do not Be Afraid

But when Simon Peter saw the boats filled with fish, he fell down at Jesus' knees. . . . When they had brought their boats to shore, they left everything and followed Jesus.

Luke 5:8a, 11

Fishing boats by the sea

These boats are perhaps like the ones Peter, James, and John were fishing in when Jesus called them. What would it be like to sit in a boat like these with your friends?

What do you think it might have been like to go fishing with Peter, James, and John—and Jesus? If you had been fishing all day and hadn't caught any fish would you feel like going home, or trying one more time?

Jesus chose Peter, James, and John to be disciples because they believed what he said when he told them to throw their nets in the water one more time. Jesus thought they would be able to share their belief with other people to help them believe in Jesus as well.

What shall we say to you, our God—

You have called us
from far and near.
You have made us—
great and small,
each one of us different
in heart and face,
but all of us your people.
We ask you, then,
make new people of us
who hear your voice
with living hearts.
Do this today and never take
your hands away from us.

Huub Oosterhuis, *Open Your Hearts*, trans. David Smith (New York: Crossroad, 1971), 21, 23. Used by permission

Tú Has Venido a la Orilla

Music: Cesáreo Gabaraín, 1979
Harm. Skinner Chávez-Melo, 1987

Spanish words: Cesáreo Gabaraín, 1979; alt.
Trans. Madeleine Forell Marshall, 1989; alt.

1 Tú has ve-ni-do a la o-ri-lla, no has bus-ca-do ni a sa-bios, ni a ri-cos, tan só-lo quie-res que yo te si-ga.
2 Tú sa-bes bien lo que ten-go: en mi bar-ca no hay o-ro ni es-pa-das; tan só-lo re-des y mi tra-ba-jo.
1 You have come down to the lake-shore seek-ing nei-ther the wise nor the wealth-y, But on-ly ask-ing for me to fol-low.
2 You know full well my pos-ses-sions. Nei-ther trea-sure nor weap-ons for con-quest, Just these my fish-nets and will for work-ing.

Estribillo (Refrain)

Je-sús, me has mi-ra-do a los o-jos; son-ri-en-do, has di-cho mi nom-bre; en la a-re-na he de-ja-do mi bar-ca; jun-to a tí bus-ca-ré o-tro mar.
O Je-sus, you have looked in-to my eyes; kind-ly smil-ing, you've called out my name. On the sand I have a-ban-doned my small boat; now with you, I will seek oth-er seas.

3 Tú necesitas mis manos,
  mi cansancio que a otros descanse,
  amor que quiera seguir amando.
  Estribillo

4 Tú, Pescador de otros mares,
  ansia eterna de almas que esperan.
  Amigo bueno, que así me llamas.
  Estribillo

3 You need my hands, my exhaustion,
  working love for the rest of the weary—
  A love that's willing to go on loving.
  Refrain

4 You who have fished other waters;
  you, the longing of souls that are yearning:
  As loving Friend, you have come to call me.
  Refrain

❧ *at* **Home**

❧ Your child is learning about things that Jesus did and said during his ministry as outlined during the Epiphany season. Most of all, your child is realizing that Jesus is always present. This can be a great comfort for children.

❧ Perhaps we as parents and caregivers would like to always be there for our children, but we can't. There are too many demands placed on us from our work and other requirements of life. And children must begin to learn how to function

❧ and make decisions without us.

This week, you might remind your child of your interest and affection by placing a note in a lunchbox or pencil box. It could be a picture of a happy event, a new joke, or just a short, thoughtful note. Children love surprises and your child is certain to notice the extra effort you made just to be present. If a note is not possible, remember to use kind words and a hug for affirmation.

Blessed Are You!

Jesus looked up at the disciples and said: "Blessed are you who are poor, for yours is the dominion of God. Blessed are you who are hungry now, for you will be filled. Blessed are you who weep now, for you will laugh."

Luke 6:20-21

Children Pray

Some children pray before going to bed. Others pray at mealtime.

God listens to prayer at all times. You never have to wait for a certain time to pray.

The Bible Tells of God's Great Love

Words: Betty Doughman, 1961; alt. 1983

Music from Thomas Este's
Whole Book of Psalms, 1592

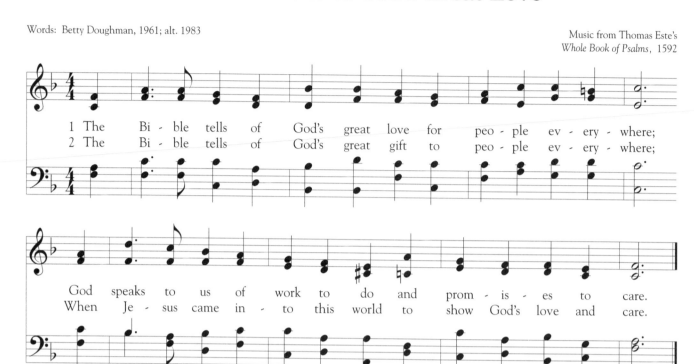

1 The Bi-ble tells of God's great love for peo-ple ev-ery-where;
2 The Bi-ble tells of God's great gift to peo-ple ev-ery-where;

God speaks to us of work to do and prom-is-es to care.
When Je-sus came in-to this world to show God's love and care.

Blessed are the **poor**...

Blessed are the **hungry**...

Blessed are those who **weep**...

For they are loved by **God!**

at **Home**

Usually young children have generous natures. At times when they are asking for things in a store, it may not seem so and certainly much has been written about the self-centered aspects of childhood. But this would be a good week to encourage the side of your child that gives freely. In Luke 6:20-21, Jesus teaches us to focus on God through prayer and on others through outreach. Try to put these into practice.

Outreach does not always demand great effort to make a global difference. That would be marvelous, of course, but don't allow yourself to feel frustrated by thinking of problems on a global scale. It would be better this week to plan some action on a local level.

Perhaps you might use the Valentine image to send a token of caring to some people in the hospital or in a nursing home. You and your child might be able to think of ideas for simple, handmade creations. The smallest efforts are often appreciated the most.

Say prayers with your child. As you plan to say a table blessing, consider choosing or making up a new grace. If you don't regularly say grace, start a new family practice. Bedtime is another time of day when you and your child can share your thoughts with God.

No Strings Attached

Then Joseph said to his brothers, "Come closer to me. . . I am your brother, Joseph, whom you sold into Egypt. And now do not be distressed, or angry with yourselves . . . for God sent me before you to preserve life."

Genesis 45:4-5

Marc Chagall, *Joseph Recognized by His Brothers*, c. 1931, The Jewish Museum, New York.
© 1993 ARS, New York/ADAGP, Paris. Used by permission.

Joseph Meets His Brothers

Joseph recognizes his brothers when they came to see him in Egypt. He was the last person they ever expected to see. They thought they would never seen him again after they sold him into slavery.

Even though Joseph could have been very angry with them, he wasn't. He greeted them with love and forgave them for what they had done. They had a wonderful reunion.

The Bible Tells of God's Great Love

The Bible tells of God's great love
For people ev'rywhere;
God speaks to us of work to do
And promises to care.

The Bible tells of God's great gift
To people ev'rywhere;
When Jesus came into this world
To show God's love and care.

Betty Doughman, from *Songs and Hymns for Primary Children*. Words © 1961 by W. L. Jenkins, renewed 1991. Used by permission of Westminster/John Knox.

Stories on the Walls

This painting is like many that were found on the walls of the tombs of the pharaohs of Egypt. The painting shows a man holding a staff in front of a table of food. He is dressed as Joseph might have been dressed. The pictures on the walls of the tomb

are lists of his duties. The drawing suggests that he was in charge of many things. All of the paintings on the inside of pyramid tombs told stories about the lives of the people who were buried there.

at **Home**

People are gifts from God. This week talk about people with your child—how different they are, how much the same they are, how we can all get along together. You may also wish to reinforce the importance of forgiveness.

In this week's Bible reading, Joseph's people were his family in Canaan. Then he ended up in Egypt and saved those people from famine. They became his people too.

Children confront many issues on a daily basis that have to do with personal relationships. Most of the time, the issues are short-lived and they may never tell you about them. Children group and regroup repeatedly.

Try to find time this week to inquire about your child's friends. Sometimes a specific question such as "Is Nat still walking home with you?" produces more results than a general one. If you get the opportunity, help your child to sort through various choices in responding to friends. For example, "What could you say to let Sam know that you still like him?"

Tell your child about a best friend you once had. Your experiences could be just the example your child needs.

Transfigured

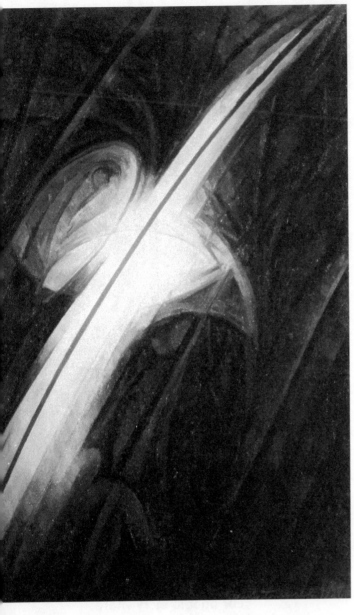

van Kudriashev, *Luminescence*, 1926, The George Costakis Collection (owned by Art Co., Ltd.). Used by permission.

Jesus took with him Peter and John and James, and went up on the mountain to pray. And while Jesus was praying, the appearance of his face changed, and his clothes became dazzling white. . . . Then from the cloud came a voice that said, "This is my Child, my Chosen!"

Luke 9:28b-29, 35

A Bright Light as a Reminder

This picture is called *Luminescence*. It has a bright light that flashes across a dark background. Its shape and brightness suggest that the darkness has changed because a light has entered into it.

It is a bit like the world when Jesus entered into it and was transfigured— or bathed in light—as God said the words, "This is my chosen one."

Tiny Pieces Make a Whole Picture

This picture is a mosaic, which means that the artist used small bits of stone or colored glass. Why did the artist use white for Jesus' robes? What do you think the disciple at the lower left corner of the picture is thinking?

Byzantine mosaic, *The Transfiguration*, c. 1100, Monastery of Daphni (near Athens), Greece (Art Resource, N.Y.). Used by permission.

at Home

This week's lesson is about changes and action. The following are some suggestions for exploring these concepts during the week.

One of the biggest changes that your child is aware of is her or his own growth. Discuss with your child the ways in which he or she has changed and grown. Ask your child, "Do you remember . . ." questions.

Your child may be less aware of changes that occur in his or her outlook. You, however, are probably very aware of them. Perhaps there are things that your child used to be afraid of or used to dislike that you can talk about. Give your child some examples from your life to encourage a free exchange of ideas.

People change, too, through acquiring knowledge. In learning about Jesus' life, your child is also learning that people can effect changes through their actions. If you could change something, what would it be? (Consider first what you truly would like to change, not the feasibility of changing it.)

Ask your child this same question. Brainstorm the problem with your child. Make a plan, within your means, to do something to make it better. Make a plan to act. And then, do it. It is important to show children early in their lives that they have good ideas, that they have ability, and that they can make a difference.

The Bible Tells of God's Great Love!

The Bible tells of God's great love
For people ev'rywhere;
God speaks to us of work to do
And promises to care.

The Bible tells of God's great gift
To people ev'rywhere;
When Jesus came into this world
To show God's love and care.

Betty Doughman, from *Songs and Hymns for Primary Children*. Words © 1961 by W. L. Jenkins, renewed 1991. Used by permission of Westminster/John Knox.

Meeting **Temptation**

Jesus, full of the Holy Spirit, returned from the Jordan and was led by the Spirit in the wilderness, where for forty days he was tempted by the devil.

Luke 4:1-2a

A Prayer

Thank you, God, for your love.

Thank you for guiding us when we meet temptation.

Thank you for helping us do what is right.

Thank you for being with us. Amen.

I Want Jesus to Walk with Me

Words: African-American spiritual

African-American spiritual

Purple is the liturgical color for the season of Lent. Throughout this season, you may wish to emphasize this color and connect the color to the season of the church year.

Think of ways to help your child experience this color.

Use these or your own ideas:

- Finger paint with purple. Put red fingerpaint on one half of the paper and blue fingerpaint on the other half. Invite your child to mix the right-hand color and left-hand color together and watch what happens.
- Try a "purple hunt." See how many purple things can be found in your house, in the yard, or on a walk. If you live in an area where signs of spring are apparent, look for purple flowers.
- Think about helping your child find something purple to wear to church one Sunday during Lent.
- Learn the prayer on the other side of this sheet and say it with your child.

▶ *at* **Home**

Younger elementary children are learning to distinguish right from wrong, good from bad. Usually they want to do the right thing. But sometimes they are tempted by what they want or by what others ask them to do. Sometimes powerful feelings of anger or frustration overwhelm them, too. "I just didn't think," may be the tearful response of a second-grader who has just done something wrong following a busy school day.

You can help your child learn to deal with his or her overwhelming feelings in acceptable ways. A "no-hitting" rule just did not work for seven-year-old Anna. Whenever she got angry or frustrated at school, she would attack her brother as soon as she was at home. A new "no-hitting people" rule worked better for her because she could direct her hitting at her large toy monkey. "Hit your monkey," her brother would often tell her. That direction gave Anna something she could do to express her frustration. What are the rules and limits for expressing anger in your family? Talk with your child about what is acceptable and what is not acceptable.

Challenged

Jesus said, "How often have I desired to gather your children together as a hen gathers her brood under her wings."

Luke 13:34

Scripture Dialogue
Based on Luke 13:31-34

Reader: Jesus, Jesus! Get away from here!

Children: Stop! What is wrong?

Reader: Jesus, Jesus! Get away from here! You are in danger!

Children: What *is* wrong?

Reader: Herod wants to kill you!

Children: No way. I can't stop!

Reader: You are in danger!

Children: I have work to do. Go and tell Herod that I have work to do.

Reader: He will kill you!

Children: Tell that fox that I will finish my work. I love my people—I must gather them. I love my children—I must gather them. I must do the work of God.

Children speak a Jesus

Kathe Kollwitz, *Seed Corn Must Not Be Ground*, © 1993 ARS, New York/UG Bild-Kunst, Bonn, Germany. Used by permission.

I Want Jesus to Walk with Me

When I'm in trouble, oh walk with me;

When I'm in trouble, oh walk with me;

When my head is bowed in sorrow,

Oh I want Jesus to walk with me.

African-American spiritual

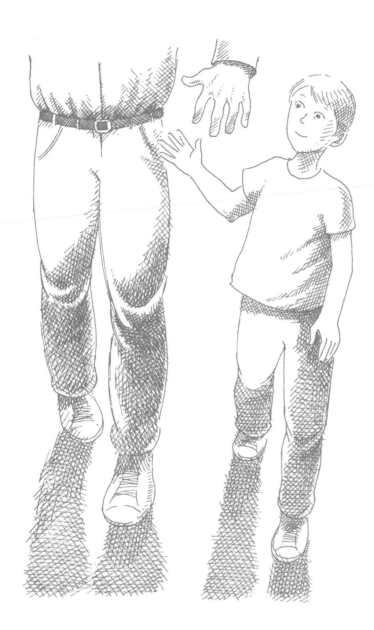

Prayer from the Psalm

Teach me your way, O God.

Lead me on your path.

Help me face challenges and not give up.

Be with me when I face people who talk

behind my back

and say things that are not true,

or people who want violence.

I believe your way is the path of goodness

and love, God.

Help me be strong.

Give my heart courage.

Teach me your way, O God.

Amen.

Based on Psalm 27:11-14

▶ *at* **Home**

Families in our time are challenged in many ways. They face many pressures. With so many expectations and so many voices making demands, a family can lose track of its identity and mission.

Whatever the shape and size of a family, its role is to be the dwelling place of God—the dwelling place of love. Families face the challenge to remember that identity.

A family is a power center that generates love between its adults and children. To participate in a family is patiently to persist in wearing down hatred with love. All this is possible if a family is looking together in the same direction—toward God. For love comes from God. The love that we feel for our family members is God's gift, and a trust, to us. It is ours to experience and share within our own families and among all the people of God's family.

Free to Rejoice

She was bent over and was quite unable to stand up straight. When Jesus saw her, he called her over and said, "Woman, you are set free from your ailment." When he laid his hands on her, immediately she stood up straight and began praising God.

Luke 13:11b-13

Judith Oelfke Smith, *Jesus Freeing Crippled Woman*, 1993, commissioned work. Used by permission.

Free to Rejoice Chant

Sometimes I feel so low. (crouch down low)
Can't do anything, no!
I'm feeling bad,
Feeling really, really sad. (make a sad face)
Sometimes I feel so low.
Sometimes I feel so low.
I'm working kind of slow.
I feel unloved, (hang head low)
Or like I just got shoved. (fall over)
Sometimes I feel so low.
Then comes a helping hand; (lift head)
That hand helps me stand. (smile)
I want to rejoice, (stand up)
Sing with all my voice,
God's love is in that hand.
When God's love touches me,
Then I can really see, (look around)
When feeling low,
Or working slow,
There's a promise of a different me. (stand up straight)
There's a promise of a different me,
And I am really free, (jump up)
Free to rejoice,
Sing with all my voice.
God's love has set me free. (reach out arms)

The Bible Tells of God's Great Love

Words: Betty Doughman, 1961; alt. 1983

Music from Thomas Este's
Whole Book of Psalms, 1592

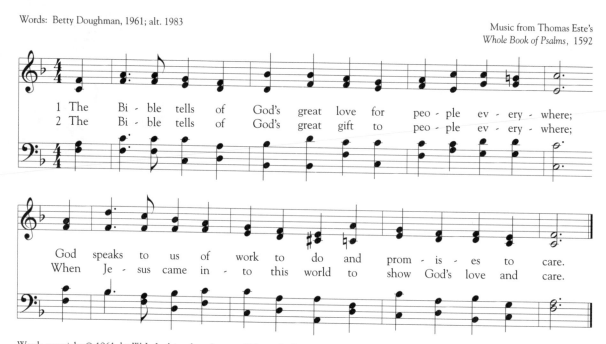

1 The Bi - ble tells of God's great love for peo - ple ev - ery - where;
2 The Bi - ble tells of God's great gift to peo - ple ev - ery - where;

God speaks to us of work to do and prom - is - es to care.
When Je - sus came in - to this world to show God's love and care.

The Bible story and this song remind us of the power of God's love. We are free from burdens, free to rejoice, free to become the person God created us to be.

▶ *at* Home

Childhood is not the free, unburdened time adults sometimes imagine it to be. Children carry burdens and fears. Some are known to parents, but children struggle with other fears on their own. Children struggle to grow up, to learn, to succeed, to find friends, and to be accepted. Children in our time struggle with difficult issues including drugs, world-wide violence, AIDS, and the fear that the earth is dying.

As parents and caregivers, we have been freed by the love of God to rejoice. We know that even when we have to carry our children's burdens as well as our own, we are still free to rejoice in our children and in the good news of God's love.

Taking the Gospel to others

Try to find the time to talk with your child about one way you both might reach out to another. Try to enable your child to carry out a kind deed or a special expression of care.

• Help your child make and send a card to a shut-in friend from church, a lonely neighbor, or a grandparent.

• Help your child call a lonely friend or relative on the phone.

Welcome Home

Rembrandt van Rijn, *The Return of the Prodigal Son*, 1636, The Hermitage Museum, St. Petersburg, Russia (Scala/Art Resource, N.Y.). Used by permission.

Welcome

Sumalubong nang magiliw *(Tagalog)*
Ha'ruch ha'ba *(Hebrew)*
Fogadni *(Hungarian)*
Bien venido *(Spanish)*
Willkommen *(German)*

So the younger son set off and went to his father. But while he was still far off, his father saw him and was filled with compassion; he ran and put his arms around him and kissed him.

Luke 15:20

Rebus Story Prayer

God me.

When I am 😠 ,

When I ,

When I am too hungry or tired,

When I have any kind of trouble,

God me.

God welcomes me.

Sumalubong nang magiliw;

Ha'ruch ha'ba; Fogadni;

Bien venido; Willkommen

God always me.

God is always with me.

Little Children, Welcome

Words: Fred Pratt Green, 1973

Music: Roy Hopp, 1988

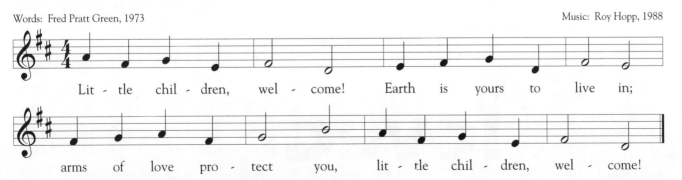

Lit- tle chil- dren, wel- come! Earth is yours to live in;

arms of love pro- tect you, lit- tle chil- dren, wel- come!

The story of unconditional love is one of the messages children need and long to hear. It is the core of the gospel. They are loved—in spite of the mistakes they make, at those times when things just don't work out, when they don't know where to turn. Each child is a beloved child of God. Children and adults alike are all "welcomed home." We are loved and affirmed by God.

It isn't always easy to let our children make mistakes and find their way back home. Reflect on ways you can let your child have freedom to make choices. Find areas of your family life where you can live with the consequences if he or she fails.

SUGGESTED READING

- Barbara Shook, *Even If I Did Something Awful* (New York: Atheneum, 1981).
  This is the story of forgiveness, reassurance, and love that endures all things — even a broken vase. When a football accidentally breaks the vase, the girl asks, "Mommy do you love me?" She then proceeds to imagine awful things that might happen and each time her mother affirms her love for her daughter. In this story, children can hear that although a parent may get angry and even yell, love does not end.

- Robert Munsch, *Love You Forever* (Scarborough, Ontario, Canada: Firefly Books, 1986).
  This is a simple, touching book about love passed on from generation to generation. The story helps children recognize that love is stronger than various difficult stages of life and that it is ultimately stronger than death.

Share a book

with your child

as you remind

him or her that he or she

is truly loved.

Jesus or the Poor?

Mary took a pound of costly perfume, put some of it on Jesus' feet, and wiped them with her hair. The house was filled with the fragrance of the perfume.

John 12:3

Archbishop Tutu is a South African leader in the Anglican church. He speaks against prejudice and for justice.

Office of Communication, United Church of Christ. Used by permission.

Devotion

We are Christian not only in church on Sunday.
Our Christianity is not something we put on, like our Sunday best, only for Sundays.
It is for every day. We are Christians from Monday to Monday. . . .
We are Christians at play, at work and at prayer. . . .
The wise men came to the Child and worshiped.
Then they gave Him their gifts.
We . . . worship our God . . . and serve [Christ] by serving our neighbor.

Desmond Tutu, *Hope and Suffering* (Grand Rapids: William B. Eerdmans Publishing Company, 1984), 148.

▶ *at* **Home**

The focus experience for this lesson is on *devotion*. The children heard what devotion can mean in the story of Mary, who anointed the feet of Jesus with costly perfume. She did this out of devotion for him.

The children are also introduced to Bishop Desmond Tutu, whose work for peace is done out of devotion for God.

Special book about devotion.

Here is a children's book about devotion you may wish to read with your child: Eloise Greenfield, *First Pink Light* (New York: Thomas Y. Crowell Company, 1976)

Palm Branches and a Cross

Then they brought it to Jesus;

and after throwing their cloaks

on the colt, they set Jesus on it."

Luke 19:28-40

Blessed is the one who comes!
Hosanna!
Glory in the highest heaven.

El Salvador Cross

▶ *at* **Home**

Easter is coming. Lent and Palm Sunday
have moved us into this very special time
in the church. Easter is a season of joy and
faith. Yet sometimes what we experience
and believe as adults is hard to share
with our children. Our own experiences of new beginnings and resurrection moments may be difficult to put
into words. It is not easy to talk
about or explain resurrection.
Sometimes, it simply becomes easier to think about Easter bunnies
and hunting for eggs.

Too often we don't share much at all about Easter. We allow it to
become a cute holiday with stuffed toys and bright clothes.

If you dye Easter eggs, talk with your children about this Easter symbol. Eggs appear to be not much more than a rock. Then a new life
breaks its way out of that shell. Eggs have long been a symbol of new
life and new beginnings.

Share the symbols of Easter as you seek to share the promise of resurrection with your children.

Weep No More

Jesus said to her, "Mary!" She turned and responded in Hebrew, "Rabbouni!" (which means Teacher).

John 20:15-16

Easter Benediction

Leader: Fly free as the butterfly.
Children: Spread your wings.
Leader: Spread your love.
Children: Christ is risen.
Leader: Christ is risen indeed.
Children: Alleluia!
Leader: Amen.

at **Home**

We are Easter people, our faith proclaims.
Perhaps nowhere is that affirmation of faith
more evident than in our children.
Children truly are "Easter people"!

There are many symbols of Easter—of the
Resurrection and new life: eggs, flowers,
butterflies, the empty cross. Yet children
embody new life and hope best of all.

The Bible Tells
of God's Great Love

Words: Betty Doughman, 1961; alt. 1983

Music from Thomas Este's
Whole Book of Psalms, 1592

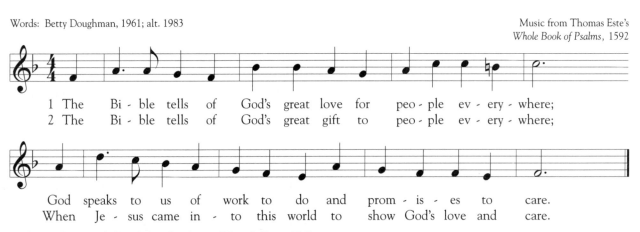

1 The Bi - ble tells of God's great love for peo - ple ev - ery - where;
2 The Bi - ble tells of God's great gift to peo - ple ev - ery - where;

God speaks to us of work to do and prom - is - es to care.
When Je - sus came in - to this world to show God's love and care.

Peace Be with You

Children write about peace:

Peace is something big.
Peace is in our hearts.
It's in our minds we sing.
It's something that has no parts.
Live in peace, or friendship at least.
Peace; make something of it, please!

Denise Wright
age 11

It was evening on that day, the first day of the week, and the doors of the house where the disciples had met were locked for fear of the religious authorities. Jesus came and stood among them and said, "Peace be with you."

John 20:19

PEACE IS PRAYING.

SIOBHAIN
AGE 6

I want peace
I like peace. I love God. Peace is the sea coral.
Peace is not pollution
So the coral can live.
I like WHALES.
I want everything to live.

Gurumittar Singh, age 6

Peace is love that is passed on from generation to generation.

Kariena Harmon
age 9

Gerald G. Jampolsky, ed., *Children as Teachers of Peace* (Berkeley: Celestial Arts, 1982).
Used by permission.

75

Colorful Creator

Text: Ruth Duck, 1992
Music: Carlton Young, 1992

Peace be with you.

Au-thor of our jour-ney, God of near and far,

praise for tale and dra-ma tell-ing who we are,

strip-ping to the es-sence strug-gles of our day,

times of change and con-flict when we choose our way.

✳ *at* Home

Peace be with you. And with your children.

Eight-year-old Clifford knows that "peace is love that is passed on from genera-tion to generation." In this Easter season, as we hear again the good news of a living Christ, may we accept Christ's gift of peace. And share it.

Jesus appeared to his disciples to reassure them, to comfort them, and to give them peace. Sometimes our children need the same kind of reassurance. In times of new learning and growing, children may be filled with self-doubt. A gentle touch and the words, "peace, my child" may sometimes offer the reassur-ance a child needs. Perhaps you can share these words with your child. Perhaps the message needs to be conveyed in your own words.

Take time to talk with your child about what peace means. As well as receiving the gift of peace, children can also be "teachers of peace." A girl, just a little older than your child, wrote these words about being a "teacher of peace."

If I were a teacher to the world's leaders about peace I'd probably say, "Go out into the world, love and cherish each living creature. Forgive and forget each mistake. Help when people need help. Reach out and give all you have. Take them to church and learn about God. Don't let one child be on the good side of you. Let each child feel like a prince or princess in your presence."

Come, Have Breakfast

When they had gone ashore, they saw a charcoal fire there, with fish on it, and bread. . . . Jesus said to them, "Come and have breakfast."

John 21:9-12a

To give thanks.

God, I thank you for the blessings and gifts
that you have provided
for me and my relatives and the food
that you have provided also.
I pray that we will receive strength and
good health from it.

Lakota grace

We come to join in the banquet of love.
Let it open our hearts and break down the
fears that keep us from loving each other.

sung by Dominican nuns

Deep peace of the shining star to you, deep
peace of the running wave to you,
deep peace of the quiet earth to you,
deep joy of the leaping fire to you, deep
peace of the Son of Peace to you.

Celtic prayer

Marcia Kelly and Jack Kelly, *One Hundred Graces*, (New York: Crown Publishers, 1992), 32.

Table Grace

Thank you, God, for happy hearts,

for rain and sunny weather.

Thank you, God, for this, our food,

and that we are together. Amen.

Tu Has Venido a la Orilla

Music: Cesáreo Gabaraín, 1979
Harm. Skinner Chávez-Melo, 1987

Spanish words: Cesáreo Gabaraín, 1979; alt.
Trans. Madeleine Forell Marshall, 1989; alt.

1 Tú has ve- ni- do a la o- ri- lla, no has bus- ca- do ni a
2 Tú sa- bes bien lo que ten- go: en mi bar- ca no hay
1 You have come down to the lake- shore seek- ing nei- ther the
2 You know full well my pos- ses- sions. Nei- ther trea- sure nor

sa- bios, ni a ri- cos, tan só- lo quie- res que yo te si- ga.
o- ro ni es- pa- das; tan só- lo re- des y mi tra- ba- jo.
wise nor the wealth- y, But on- ly ask- ing for me to fol- low.
weap- ons for con- quest, Just these my fish- nets and will for work- ing.

Estribillo (Refrain)

Je- sús, me has mi- ra- do a los o- jos; son- ri- en- do,
O Je- sus, you have looked in- to my eyes; kind- ly smil- ing,

has di- cho mi nom- bre; en la a- re- na he de- ja- do mi
you've called out my name. On the sand I have a- ban- doned my

bar- ca; jun- to a tí bus- ca- ré o- tro mar.
small boat; now with you, I will seek oth- er seas.

3 Tú necesitas mis manos,
    mi cansancio que a otros descanse,
    amor que quiera seguir amando.
        Estribillo

4 Tú, Pescador de otros mares,
    ansia eterna de almas que esperan.
    Amigo bueno, que así me llamas.
        Estribillo

3 You need my hands, my exhaustion,
    working love for the rest of the weary—
    A love that's willing to go on loving.
        Refrain

4 You who have fished other waters;
    you, the longing of souls that are yearning:
    As loving Friend, you have come to call me.
        Refrain

at **Home**

Christ offers forgiveness to Peter and the invitation to new life to all. The Christian's response to Christ's forgiveness and invitation to new life is gratitude. Saying grace at mealtime is one way of responding to the ways in which we are fed by the living Christ.

Share one or more of the following table graces at mealtimes during the next week. Consider learning one of them to use regularly. Taking time to learn a new table grace can help children and adults think about the gratitude they are offering.

Shepherd Psalm

⭐ **God is my shepherd, I shall not want.**

Psalm 23:1

An Interview with Heather— A Shepherd Who Is Your Age

Question: **How long have you had sheep, Heather?**

Answer: We have always had sheep, as long as I can remember.

Q: **How old were you when you got a lamb of your own?**

A: I was seven.

Q: **What do you do when a lamb is born?**

A: Usually you don't have to do too much right away, because they suck on their mother. But you have to watch out for them. One time, we were gone, and one of our mother sheep had twins. The first lamb that was born, we called her Callie, crawled behind the hay. When we came home, we could only find one lamb. Then my brother, Shane, found Callie behind the hay and pulled her out of there. We took her in the house to put her under a red light (heat lamp) until she was warm enough to go out to her mother.

The Good Shepherd, c. 250 C.E., in Cubiculum Velatio, Catacomb of Priscilla, Rome. Used by permission of Commissione Pontificiale per Archeologia Sacra, Città Vaticano, Italy. Used by permission.

 This drawing of the Good Shepherd was painted on the inside of a family tomb hundreds of years ago. See how he gently carries a sheep across his shoulders. Perhaps this sheep had been lost and he is carrying it home.

continued on next page

Q: **What do you do to take care of sheep?**

A: Give them grain, hay, and water.

Q: **Do they ever get in trouble?**

A: Yes. Lane, our little baby lamb, put his head through the fence and got stuck. He was baa-ing his head off when I found him. I was scared. I didn't know what to do. I had to take his head down to the bigger end of the fence and gently twist it to get it out of there.

Q: **What does it mean to be a shepherd?**

A: Watch over the sheep and keep them safe.

Q: **What does the psalm "God is my shepherd, I shall not want" mean to you?**

A: God takes care of us. And we shouldn't ask for too much— sometimes we want too much.

Heather Endicott, Meridian, Idaho

at **Home**

The focus of this week's "Liturgy of Learning" is to explore ways that the Twenty-third Psalm has sustained and still sustains people of faith and provides a good opportunity for cross-generational conversation between your child and those of different ages in your family. If you were familiar with this psalm as a child, share your memories of it with your child. Perhaps you have memorized it or sung it. Perhaps you remember a grandparent or other elder reading or reciting it to you.

Help your child to talk with other family members, especially those of other generations such as grandparents and great-grandparents about their memories or associations with this psalm.

All Things New

Then I saw a new heaven and a new earth; for the first heaven and the first earth had passed away, and the sea was no more. And I heard a loud voice say, "See, I am making all things new."

Revelation 21:1

Choi Hyun-Joo, *Jerusalem*, 1976, in *Children of the World Paint Jerusalem* (New York: Bantam Book, published by arrangement with Keter Publishing House Jerusalem Ltd., 1978). © The Israel Museum, Jerusalem. Used by permission.

When we think of making old houses or furniture look new we sometimes think of painting them. Sometimes when we think of making the earth new we think of what it would look like. The person who wrote today's Bible verse paints a picture with words about a new world. How would you paint a picture of a new world?

Morning Stars Start a New Day

A morning star appears just before the dawn of a new day. When it appears in the sky it is a sign that the night is coming to an end and a new day is about to begin. Over the years many songs and poems have been written about the morning star.

The Sioux Nation (Plains Indians of North America) has used the symbol of the morning star for many years. Now they have begun to make quilts that have the design of a morning star on them. The designs often look like the one above.

at Home

As we look toward our children's future, it is impossible to imagine what they will face in the years ahead. Their lives are threatened by AIDS, drug use, violence, and environmental damage. Children are aware of the problems in the world in which they are growing up. They may feel power-less, and therefore hopeless, as they confront these problems. "I wish the earth wasn't dying, but I think it is," an elementary school child sadly told his mother. At times, it is also difficult for adults not to feel hopeless thinking about our children's future.

We need to share together the message of hope for the future. Children and adults need the reassur-ance of God's presence, creating all things new.

Families can take on the challenge to imagine God's new world and be inspired to live toward it. Working together on a volunteer project in the community or at church can help children feel that they are "living toward" God's world. Consider vol-unteering together to visit a shut-in, care for a younger child, work at a soup kitchen, or share in a community clean-up day.

Take time to listen to your children's concerns about and dreams for the future. Their dreams may range from "I dream nobody would make fun of me" to "I dream I could discover the cure for AIDS." As they share their hopes and dreams, they begin to "envision God's new world."

When children hear God's promise of a "new day," they may be able to gain the confidence to face the tough times in which they are growing up. Then they can live and work toward the realm of God. We cannot give our children a problem-free child-hood, but we can offer them hope and the good news of God's presence now and in the future.

Open Heart, Open Home

A certain woman named Lydia,

a worshiper of God, was listening to us.

. . . God opened her heart to listen

eagerly to what was said by Paul. . . .

When she and her household were

baptized, she urged us, saying, "If you

have judged me to be faithful to the

Savior, come and stay at my home."

And she prevailed upon us.

Acts 16:14-15

A Dramatic Reading*

Narrator: **I am the narrator. I will tell you about the travels of Paul and Timothy.**

Paul: I am Paul.

Timothy: I am Timothy. Paul and I are missionaries.

Narrator: **Paul and Timothy and their friends traveled with the good news of Christ. They went from town to town. The churches they visited grew stronger. One night Paul had a dream.**

Paul: In my dream, I saw a man saying "come and help us."

Timothy: So Paul and I and our friends sailed to a town called Philippi. We stayed there for a few days.

Narrator: **On the sabbath day, they went down by the river to a place of prayer. They sat down and spoke to the women who were there.**

Timothy: Greetings.

Paul: We want to share the news of Jesus Christ.

Narrator: **Timothy and Paul talked about Jesus and the women listened.**

Lydia: I am Lydia. I worship God. I am a business woman. I sell purple cloth, good purple cloth.

Narrator: **As Lydia listened to the words of Paul and Timothy, God opened her heart.**

Lydia: I want to be baptized and all of my household with me.

Paul: Lydia, I am glad to baptize you and your household in the name of Jesus Christ.

Narrator: **Lydia and her household were baptized. After the baptism, Lydia spoke again to Paul.**

Lydia: If you think I am faithful to God, come and stay at my home.

Narrator: **Paul and Timothy went to stay with Lydia. Lydia opened her heart to God's love. She opened her home to God's messengers. Lydia welcomed Christ and she welcomed others.**

*Note: This script can also be read as a story.

The following rhyme tells Lydia's story. Each time the rhyme has the word "Lydia," read all together. Clap on each beat of her name. A drum, wood blocks, or other percussion instruments may also be used to emphasize the beats of her name. Take turns reading the lines that tell her story. The whole group joins together every time **"Ly-di-a"** is chanted.

Say a Rhyme

Ly-di-a, Ly-di-a

(clap, clap, clap, pause, clap, clap, clap)

She had an open heart.

Ly-di-a, Ly-di-a

(clap, clap, clap, pause, clap, clap, clap)

She didn't stand apart.

Ly-di-a, Ly-di-a

(clap, clap, clap, pause, clap, clap, clap)

She heard Paul's good news.

Ly-di-a, Ly-di-a

(clap, clap, clap, pause, clap, clap, clap)

God's love changed her views.

Ly-di-a, Ly-di-a

(clap, clap, clap, pause, clap, clap, clap)

Said, "Won't you come and stay?"

Ly-di-a, Ly-di-a,

(clap, clap, clap, pause, clap, clap, clap)

Opened her home that day.

Ly-di-a, Ly-di-a

(clap, clap, clap, pause, clap, clap, clap)

at **Home**

Hospitality is a biblical theme in both the Old and New Testaments. Christ welcomes strangers, invites the unworthy, and accepts the hospitality of others.

Yet today hospitality is difficult to practice. In our society, there are many reasons to fear strangers. We know it is not wise to pick up strangers in our cars or to invite strangers into our homes. Sometimes our busy lives even prevent families from inviting in friends. Too often, it is easier to meet friends for coffee or go out to eat together than to invite others into our homes. Children need the experience of inviting others into their homes. At home, they are able to open their hearts to others as they show their favorite possessions or simply welcome others into their space.

As opportunities arise, help your child to invite others to your home. These guests may be children who are friends from school or church. They may be adult friends of the family or they may be relatives. Allow your child to be the one who issues the invitation. For example, you may suggest, "Would you like to call Aunt Carol and invite her to have pizza with us tomorrow?"

As children learn to invite others, to welcome them and share what they can offer, they are learning to practice hospitality.

Connections

One day ... we met a slave-girl who had a spirit of divination and brought her owners a great deal of money by fortune-telling.

Acts 16:16

Connect

Signs help us make connections between a law and how we are to respond. Think about a stop sign.

At many street corners the law is to stop—so there is a sign that tells people that. Here are some signs that give hints on how we should respond to God's laws.

I Want Jesus to Go With Me

Words: African-American spiritual; alt.   Music: African-American spiritual

1 I want Je - sus to go with me;
2 In my tri - als, O com - fort me;

I want Je - sus to go with me;
In my tri - als, O com - fort me;

All a - long my pil - grim jour - ney,
When my heart is al - most break - ing,

O I want Je - sus to go with me.
O I want Je - sus to com - fort me.

◆ *at* **Home**

Younger elementary children begin to encounter situations in which they see peo-ple *use* one another. They may recognize that people around them sometimes use friendships or even family relationships for personal gain, rather than respecting each one's rights and wishes. For example, your child may see another child acting friendly toward a classmate who is about to have a birthday party, without really being a friend. Often children might take offense at such behavior. They might say, "Ben isn't John's friend! He's just acting like he really likes John so he'll get invited to his party." Yet they may not be able to see the connection in their own behavior between caring for someone and allowing that person to be free.

Younger elementary children often try to control the actions of their friends, their siblings, their parents. Try to help them connect love with freedom. Point out any actions around the house that might be considered unfair or exploitative, such as one sibling bribing another not to tell when something goes wrong.

You may want to get a copy of Susan Jeschke's *Perfect the Pig* (New York: Holt, Rinehart and Winston, 1980). In the story Olive gives Perfect his freedom because she truly loves him. It serves as a reminder that through the good news of God's saving love, we are all free.

This story is also available on videotape as a part of the *Reading Rainbow* collection. State libraries have the *Reading Rainbow* videotapes. Many public libraries and school libraries also carry them. Ask for *Reading Rainbow* tape 25.

Pentecost's Many Voices

When the day of Pentecost had come … suddenly from heaven there came a sound like the rush of a violent wind, and it filled the entire house where they were sitting …. All of them were filled with the Holy Spirit.

Acts 2:1-2, 4

Emil Nolde, *The Pentecost*, 1909, Stiftung Seebull, Ada and Emil Nolde, Neukirchen, Germany. Used by permission.

Love in Many Languages

Love in any language, straight from the heart, pulls us all together, never apart; and once we learn to speak it—all the world will hear— love in any language—fluently spoken here.

Liebe
(leeb'-eh)
German

Amore
(ah-mor'-aye)
Italian

Elske
(el'-skah)
Norwegian

Love
(English)

Amor
(ah-mor')
French

The Spirit of God visited the disciples as a mighty wind and as small flames of fire. It all happened a long time ago on a day we now call Pentecost. It is a day we name as the birthday of the church.

The Bible Tells of God's Great Love

Words: Betty Doughman, 1961; alt. 1983

Music from Thomas Este's
Whole Book of Psalms, 1592

1 The Bi - ble tells of God's great love for peo - ple ev - ery - where;
2 The Bi - ble tells of God's great gift to peo - ple ev - ery - where;

God speaks to us of work to do and prom - is - es to care.
When Je - sus came in - to this world to show God's love and care.

at **Home**

Pentecost can be a great time for a family celebration. The day of Pentecost is considered the birthday of the church. Consider celebrating by having a small birthday of the Christian church party at home. Include stories about what makes your congregation special or stories about how the church has changed. Tell your children about the church you went to as a child, or what the church and Sunday school were like then.

Make a birthday cake and invite friends from church to share in the celebration. This is a time to give thanks for the church friends who help us understand the message of God's love.

During the week, pick up a Bible and read Acts 2:1-21. Ask your child what he or she remembers about the event from the Sunday school lesson.

Hope Given

Hope does not disappoint us, because God's love has been poured into our hearts through the Holy Spirit that has been given to us.

Romans 5:5

most bulbs are planted in the fall. In some parts of the country that means they are put into the ground after there has been a frost and after other growing things have died. It takes a lot of hope to put a dried out bulb into the cold earth. Those people who plant bulbs have hope that in the spring a flower will grow and bloom.

We are people of HOPE

We Are people of HOPE

We are Happy.

We are people of HOPE.

We are Open.

We are people of HOPE.

We are Peacemakers.

We are people of HOPE.

We are Eager.

We are Happy,

   Open,

   Peacemakers,

   Eager,

We are people of HOPE.

God gives HOPE!

* * * * * * * *

at **Home**

For younger elementary children, *hope* often means wishing for something, such as: "I hope I get a Nintendo for my birthday"; "I hope we can go to McDonald's"; "I hope Grandma comes to visit."

At this age, children may not associate *hope* with church or with God. Yet children express hope when they are willing to try. Children are filled with hope when they get up thinking about a game to play, a friend to see, a book to read, an adventure to create. Hope is shown in their anticipation of a new day. Children live in hope when they dream and plan about what life may be. Hope is the promise of life unfolding. Hope is the gift of the Holy Spirit.

an Alabaster jar

Jesus said to Simon, "Do you see this woman? I entered your house; you gave me no water for my feet, but she has bathed my feet with her tears and dried them with her hair."

Luke 7:36–8:3

This woman came to Jesus to have her sins forgiven. To ask for this favor she showed her respect for Jesus by washing his feet with her tears and with a special ointment she brought in an alabaster jar.

Wu Yuen-kwei, *Her Sins Are Forgiven*,
The Asian Christian Art Association,
Sakyo-ku, Kyoto, Japan. Used by permission.

91

Colorful Creator

Colorful Creator, God of mystery,

thank you for the artist

teaching us to see

glimpses of the meaning

of the commonplace,

visions of the holy

in each human face.

Ruth Duck, "Colorful Creator" (hymn),
unpublished, © 1992 by Ruth C. Duck.
Used by permission.

"I wish life had a rewind button."

**Forgiveness is the rewind button.
How do you picture forgiveness?**

at Home

Little by little, children learn about repentance and forgiveness. At first "I'm sorry" and "Am I forgiven?" are just words to get out of trouble. Adults may get frustrated when their child says, "I'm sorry," then repeats the same behavior. Over a period of time, children begin to recognize their own mistakes. There are times when they genuinely feel bad about something that has happened and want the chance to try again. Then "I'm sorry" and "Am I forgiven?" become more than words to avoid adult anger.

Little by little, children learn that honest apologies (confession) can lead to forgiveness and renewal. They learn that forgiveness provides the chance to try again.

Sometimes children have difficulty accepting forgiveness. To talk about the gifts of forgiveness and love that endures, look for the following books to share with your child:

Barbara Shook Hazen, *Even If I Did Something Awful* (New York: Atheneum, 1981). This is a story of forgiveness, reassurance, and love, which endures all things—even a broken vase. When the football accidentally breaks the vase, the girl asks, "Mommy, do you love me?" She then proceeds to imagine awful things that might happen, and each time her mother affirms her love for her daughter. In this story children can hear that although a parent might get angry and yell, love does not end.

Robert Munsch, *Love You Forever* (Scarborough, Ontario: Firefly Books, 1987). From the time of birth through adulthood, love endures all things. This is a story of the strength of love.

Hans Wilhem, *Let's Be Friends Again* (New York: Crown Publishers, 1986). When his little sister sets his pet turtle free, the boy in the story is very angry, but finally he is able to act in real forgiveness—by starting fresh.

One in Christ

There is no longer Jew or Greek, there is no longer slave or free, there is no longer male and female; for all of you are one in Christ Jesus.

Galatians 3:27-29

Norman Rockwell, *The Golden Rule*, 1961. The Norman Rockwell Museum of Stockbridge, Massachusetts. Used by permission of Curtis Archives.

All Are One

In Christ Jesus you are all children of God.
There is longer Jew
nor Greek. There is no longer slave
nor free. There is no longer male
and female.
All of you are one in Christ Jesus.
If you belong to Christ, then you are all the great-great-great
grandchildren of Abraham and Sarah.

Based on Galatians 3:27-29

The Bible Tells of God's Great Love

The Bible tells of God's great love

For people ev'rywhere;

God speaks to us of work to do

And promises to care.

The Bible tells of God's great love

To people ev'rywhere;

When Jesus came into this world

To show God's love and care.

Words © 1961 by W. L. Jenkins; from *Songs and Hymns for Primary Children*.
Used by permission of The Westminster Press

at Home

In a world that seems to be getting smaller, young children are exposed to others with different customs and languages on a daily basis. Even in rural areas, refugees may be resettled by churches and changing economics may bring in groups of ethnic workers who have not before been present.

Girls and boys need to learn respect for one another as persons rather than absorbing the stereotypical values and language of television, popular music, and advertising, which often emphasize people as objects rather than as persons. One does not have to listen long to hear seven- and eight-year-olds talking about boys who are "hunks" and girls who are "babes."

On another level, mainstreaming efforts in public education expose children to a variety of persons with disabilities. Yet, without the support of church and home, children may resent those who are "different" or who need special time and attention.

Help your child understand that in God's eyes there are no differences between people. All are a valued part of the human family. The church and family are the world's greatest hope for world peace and justice through acceptance and love of others. Please help by reminding your child to accept others just as they are.

Here are some books about human differences to share with your child:

- Peter Spier, *People*
  (New York: Doubleday, 1980).

- Mitsumasa Anno et al., *All in a Day*
  (New York: Philomel Books, 1986).

- Thomas B. Allen, *Where Children Live*
  (Englewood Cliffs, N.J.: Prentice Hall, 1980).

- Norma Simon, *Why Am I Different*
  (Chicago: Albert Whitman anCompany,1976).

Freedom to Love and Serve

Love Your Neighbor As Yourself

For the whole law is summed up in a single commandment, "You shall love your neighbor as yourself."

Galatians 5:13-14

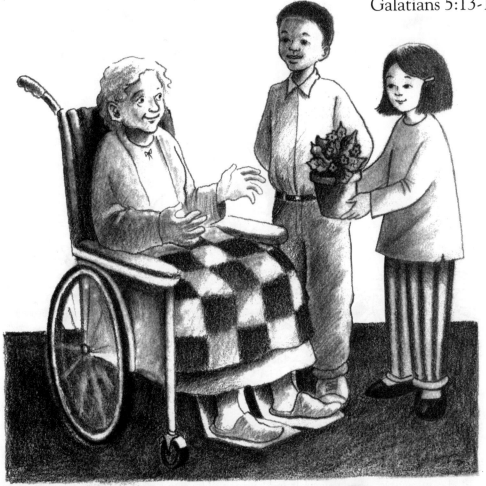

 To love your neighbor as yourself means to find ways of being kind and loving.

The Bible Tells of God's Great Love

Words: Betty Doughman, 1961; alt. 1983

Music from Thomas Este's
Whole Book of Psalms, 1592

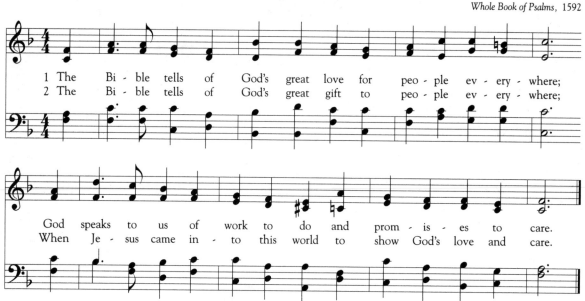

1 The Bi - ble tells of God's great love for peo - ple ev - ery - where;
2 The Bi - ble tells of God's great gift to peo - ple ev - ery - where;

God speaks to us of work to do and prom - is - es to care.
When Je - sus came in - to this world to show God's love and care.

at Home

Younger elementary children are learning to recognize other's needs and reach out to offer help. They are learning to think of needs besides their own. Learning to love and value self and learning to love and care for neighbor go hand-in-hand.

Your child can begin to share his or her love in wider circles. Help your child participate in some type of service for others. Perhaps your child could join you when are involved in serving. Perhaps there are special service or mission possibilities for children in the church or in the community. As children experience loving and serving, they will grow in understanding of the commandment, "You shall love your neighbor as yourself."

as a Mother Comforts Her Child

As a mother comforts her child, so I will comfort you; you shall be comforted in Jerusalem.

Isaiah 66:13

Mary Cassatt, *Margot Embracing Her Mother (Mother and Child)* 1902, gift of Ms. Aimee Lamb in memory of Mr. and Mrs. Horatio A. Lamb, Museum of Fine Arts, Boston.
© 1993 Museum of Fine Arts, Boston. All rights reserved. Used by permission.

Comfort, comfort little children,

God is ever here.

Comfort, comfort little children,

God erases fear.

Comfort, comfort little children,

God holds you so dear.

Comfort, comfort little children,

God's voice calls you near.

Over ninety years ago a woman named Mary Cassatt painted a picture of a little girl named Margot hugging her mother.

The mother is comforting her child, just like God comforts all of us.

97

Responsive Reading

Reader: When I am scared my mother hugs me

All: As a mother comforts her child.

Reader: When my kitty died my dad wiped my tears

All: As a mother comforts her child.

Reader: When other children laughed at me my grandmother held me on her lap

All: As a mother comforts her child.

Reader: When you are sad remember God says, "So will I comfort you"

All: As a mother comforts her child.

Reader: As a mother comforts her child, so will I comfort you. You shall be comforted. God will comfort you.

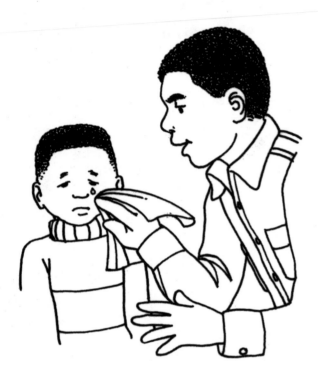

at Home

Your child has probably experienced being comforted by a mother or a father and by other family members. This week's focus scripture from Isaiah connects the experiences a child has at home with an understanding of God. It provides an opportunity to connect the love you and your child share to the loving nature of God.

Talk with your child about being comforted. Share your own experiences and memories of being comforted by your mother or father. Or share memories of the ways your child was comforted when he or she was younger. You may recall a favorite lullaby, a favorite stuffed animal, a favorite blanket, or a special trick you used to get him or her to sleep.

If your child is facing challenges or changes at this time, remind him or her that comfort is available. You can talk to your child about your support and continuing comfort. Then read the Bible verse on the front of this guide. God's comfort is available, too.

Then Amos answered Amaziah,
"I am no prophet, nor a prophet's
son. God said to me, 'Go, prophesy
to my people Israel.' "

Amos 7:14-15

Hard Words

Prophecy of Amos

Amos said, "Had another vision from God. In it I saw God standing beside a wall that had been built with the use of a plumb line, and there was a plumb line in God's hand. "

God asked me, "Amos, what do you see?"

"A plumb line," I answered.

Then God said, "I am using it to show that my people are like a wall that is out of line. I will not change my mind again about punishing them. The places where Isaac's descendants worship will be destroyed. The holy places of Israel will be left in ruins. I will bring the dynasty of King Jeroboam to an end."

Amaziah, the priest of Bethel, then sent a report to King Jeroboam of Israel. It said:

Amos is plotting against you with the people. His speeches will destroy the country. This is what he says: "Jeroboam will die in battle, and the people of Israel will be taken away from their land into exile."

Amaziah then said to Amos, "That's enough, prophet! Go on back to Judah and do your preaching there. Let them pay you for it. Don't prophesy here at Bethel anymore. This is the king's place of worship, the national temple."

Amos answered, "I am not the kind of prophet who prophesies for pay. I am a herdsman, and I take care of fig trees. But God took me from my work and ordered me to come and prophesy to the people of Israel. So listen to what God says. You tell me to stop prophesying, to stop raving against the people of Israel. And so Amaziah, God says to you, 'The people of Israel will certainly be taken away from their own land into exile.' "

◀ *at* **Home**

◀ In an often confused and confusing world, parents long for clear standards by which to teach their children right and wrong. We find nothing like a set of absolute rules, which fits every situation. Yet, there is a standard. The prophets of the Old Testament call us to that standard, the "plumb line" of God, as clearly as they called to people in their own times.

◀ As you try to teach values to your child, point them to the "plumb line" of God. Children do need guidelines. They need opportunities to talk about why certain behaviors are wrong or to discuss what led them to trouble. Repentance involves change. In order for children to make changes, they need to understand what went wrong and how to choose a better course the next time.

◀ In addition to guidelines, children need family activities. Activities that foster feelings of belonging and commitment to the family help children learn responsibility. Reading or playing together, sharing family traditions, and doing chores together all create respect for others, which is the foundation of the "plumb line" to which God calls us.

◀ Talking now about the "plumb line"—God's standard—and the guidelines you establish will lay a foundation for talking with your children as they grow to adolescence.

Justice
for the
Poor

Then God said to me, "Hear this, you that trample on the needy, and bring to ruin the poor of the land, surely I will never forget any of their deeds."

Amos 8:4, 6-7

Summer Fruit Grows Ripe

The summer fruit.

The ripe fruit will not last.

Soon it will be gone.

If it is not eaten, it will decay.

The time is at hand,

The time for justice.

As the fruit grows ripe,

Remember to seek justice for the poor.

Justice for all.

Food for all.

We eat the summer fruit.

When summer fruit ripens, it is just the right time to eat it. If it is not eaten when it is ripe, it will spoil. God told Amos that the time for justice and fairness was ripe. He showed Amos a basket of summer fruit as a reminder that the time for justice was ripe, just like the fruit.

Justice is a way of balancing.

To be *just*, we balance **fairness** and rights so that they are given equally to all people.

❧ ❧ ❧ ❧ ❧ ❧ ❧ *at* Home

Justice is not an easy concept to convey to children. Nor is it easy to involve children in the struggle for justice. Yet, they need opportunities to respond to God's call for justice.

Here are some suggestions for helping children learn about and respond to justice issues:

- Include children in social action programs, or at least point them out to children and explain what is being done and why.

- Help children get involved in actions that are within their capabilities. Start with small projects and try to make them fun.

When children have opportunities to share with others who are concerned and to witness the commitment of family members, friends, and church leaders, they can develop their own response to God's call to justice.

Remember, too, that justice is often a part of a child's daily activity. Point out situations at home where justice is an issue, such as the way children treat each other and pets. Pointing out simple situations where justice is needed can help them begin to understand the broader concept. See that justice is served at home. For example, it is unjust if one child is punished when two are guilty or one child takes something that belongs to another. Seek to be just and point out the value of justice to your child.

The Prayer of Jesus

Jesus was praying. One of the disciples said to him, "Lord, teach us to pray." Jesus said to them, "When you pray, say: Father [and Mother], hallowed be your name."

Luke 11:1-4

Jesus was praying in a certain place, and after he had finished, one of his disciples said to him, "Lord, teach us to pray, as John taught his disciples." He said to them, "When you pray, say:

"Father [and Mother], hallowed be your name. Your dominion come. Give us each day our daily bread and forgive us our sins, for we ourselves forgive everyone indebted to us. And do not bring us to the time of trial."

Matthew 6:9-13

Jesus Teaches the Disciples to Pray

at **Home**

Your child may or may not know the prayer that Jesus taught his followers. You may want to help him or her memorize this prayer. Find opportunities to use it at home.

* Use it as a table grace.

* Stick a copy of the prayer on your refrigerator (Be sure to use the wording that your church uses in worship.) Say it with your child when he or she comes into the kitchen.

* Use it as a bedtime prayer.

* Use your own ideas to help your child become familiar with this prayer.

The next time your child attends a worship service, help him or her find "The Lord's Prayer" in the hymnal to follow along as it is prayed by the congregation. Even if your child cannot yet read, this type of instruction helps to make the prayers in worship seem more familiar.

Yet it was I who taught Ephraim to walk, I took them up in my arms.
I led them with cords of human kindness, with bands of love.

Hosea 11:3-4

in God's Arms

**Hosea heard
God say,
"I taught my
child to walk."**

I loved.

I taught to walk.

I took them in my arms.

I healed.

I led them with cords of human kindness,

with bands of love.

I bent down to them and fed them.

I will return them to their homes.

God guides us all
Some children walk. Some can run.
Some glide along in a wheelchair.
Some stand with a little help from friend
God guides us all.

at **Home**

The words of Hosea 11:3-4 offer an understanding of God as comforter and guide. This is a very fitting view of God for younger elementary children. They need the understanding of a God who guides, comforts, and helps, maybe even when other help is not easily available.

At home, you can continue to keep these words before your family.
Here are some suggestions:

- Make a poster together, using words and images of Hosea 11:3-4.

- Make a paper chain. On each link, put a name of someone who offers kindness to your family. Include neighbors, friends, relatives, and teachers. Mention how God works through the "cords of human kindness."

- Visit a young child learning to walk or someone learning to walk again and talk about the patience or courage it takes. Mention God as a source of patience and courage.

By Faith

Now faith is the assurance of things hoped for, the conviction of things not seen.

Hebrews 11:1

Faith is a feeling or a belief that we have. Sometimes people say that faith is like building blocks. **As you add building blocks to a wall of blocks, the wall grows stronger. If you add faith to your life, your life could grow stronger too.**

Little Children, Welcome

Words: Fred Pratt Green, 1973

Music: SAIPAN, by Roy Hopp, 1988

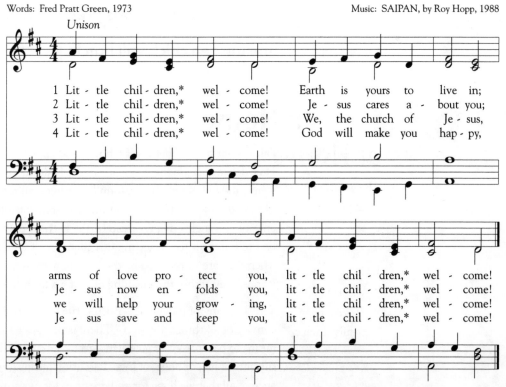

1 Lit-tle chil-dren,* wel-come! Earth is yours to live in;
2 Lit-tle chil-dren,* wel-come! Je-sus cares a-bout you;
3 Lit-tle chil-dren,* wel-come! We, the church of Je-sus,
4 Lit-tle chil-dren,* wel-come! God will make you hap-py,

arms of love pro-tect you, lit-tle chil-dren,* wel-come!
Je-sus now en-folds you, lit-tle chil-dren,* wel-come!
we will help your grow-ing, lit-tle chil-dren,* wel-come!
Je-sus save and keep you, lit-tle chil-dren,* wel-come!

*You may wish to substitute other words as appropriate; for example, "Sisters, brothers, welcome!" "Little sister, welcome!" or "Little brother, welcome!"

What we see in life helps us understand faith.

The chick is the unseen part of an egg in a nest.

The mother hen has great faith that someday

the unseen chick will hatch.

at Home

Faith is not really taught, yet families and churches strive for "faith education." How do we educate the young for lives of faithful living? Perhaps each person, young and old, simply has to form his or her own response to the call of God. Yet we also believe that surrounding children with the language and experience of faith helps them to "catch" the faith. Perhaps the passage of Hebrews best tells us how to engage in faith education. Children learn and grow in faith when they are surrounded by the faithful witness. As they hear and know the stories, they absorb the meaning of living a faith-filled life.

The scripture for today says, "Faith is the assurance of things hoped for, the conviction of things not seen." There is perhaps no better statement of what it means to be a parent or guardian—to try to raise children in love, to give them the gifts of life, of hope, of love. Parenting means living in faith—in the assurance of all that we hope for and dream of for our children and the conviction of the promise we cannot yet see, the promise of who they will become.

The Cloud of Witnesses

Therefore, since we are surrounded by so great a cloud of witnesses, let us run with perseverance the race that is set before us.

Hebrews 12:1-2

We are part of a

"great cloud of witnesses."

Witnesses are people who believe in God.

For hundreds and hundreds of years

believers have been witnesses.

The Bible Tells of God's Great Love

The Bible tells of God's great love
For people ev'rywhere;
God speaks to us of work to do
And promises to care.

The Bible tells of God's great love
To people ev'rywhere;
When Jesus came into this world
To show God's love and care.

Words © 1961 by W. L. Jenkins;
from *Songs and Hymns for Primary Children*.
Used by permission of The Westminster Press.

Sometimes life is called a "race." Races can be difficult; to run a race we need to be **strong** and able to go over or around all obstacles. Life is like that too. Sometimes it is difficult and sometimes it has many obstacles. But God is always with us to help us finish the race.

• • • • • *at* Home

The "great cloud of witnesses" is important for all of us. As parents and care-givers, we find encouragement by talking with others who have children a little older than ours. From those who have already blazed the way, we can pick up hints about parenting, about dealing with the schools, or about simply "surviving" a difficult phase.

Witnesses who have gone before and struggled with issues of faith in their time offer us the courage to face the tasks before us. A Christian community is one setting where witnesses to the faith can make connections. Older members can support and encourage young parents. Older children can support younger children just starting school. Whether the issues are "how to be a good parent" or "how to work for social justice in this community," the witness of others builds support, strength, and the courage to "run the race" before us.

The "great cloud of witnesses" is the source of strength for children. Their race will not be easy. It is a course with many challenges, such as the distribution of resources, global stewardship, and population control.

Try to help your child turn to the Christian community and to the history of those who have gone before. Recognizing that he or she is surrounded by a "great cloud of witnesses" will give your child courage and strength which he or she will need to face the road ahead.

Bless God, O my soul, and all that is within me,
bless God's holy name. God is merciful and gracious,
slow to anger and abounding in steadfast love.

Psalm 103:1, 8

all that is within me
—Bless God

Psalm of Praise

Bless God, O My soul;

And all that is within me, bless God's holy name!

Bless God, O my soul,

And remember God's blessings.

God keeps me from harm,

God crowns me with love and mercy.

God blesses you with good as long as you live.

God is merciful and gracious,

God is slow to anger and full of steadfast love.

Great is God's steadfast love.

Bless God, O my soul.

Praise God
in all you do.
Sing new songs
of praise to
God's holy
name.

▲ *at* **Home**

Praising God can happen in many ways. When you see a beautiful sunset or a bright rainbow, when your child tries hard and succeeds, when love is shared in the family, God can be praised. Take a moment to celebrate and give God thanks for courage, for beauty, for determination and strength, and above all for steadfast love.

Remind your child of God's steadfast love. God's love is with us through all kinds of trials, just as God's love guided the people of Israel.